Pieces of Purgatory

Mental Retardation
In and Out
of Institutions

Pieces of Purgatory

Mental Retardation In and Out of Institutions

J. David Smith
University of South Carolina

Brooks/Cole Publishing Company
Pacific Grove, California

Brooks/Cole Publishing Company
A Division of Wadsworth, Inc.

Printed in the United States of America
10 9 8 7 6 5 4 3 2 1

Library of Congress Cataloging-in-Publication Data
Smith, J. David
Pieces of purgatory : mental retardation in and out of institutions / J. David Smith.
p. cm.
ISBN 0-534-25206-0
1. Lovelace, John, 1931- . 2. Mental retardation facilities patients—Biography. 3. Mentally handicapped—Biography. 4. Mentally handicapped—Institutional care. I. Title.
RC570.S63 1994
362.3'092—dc20
(B) 94-17199
CIP

Sponsoring Editor: *Vicki Knight*
Marketing Representative: *Sharon Stevens*
Editorial Assistant: *Lauri Ataide*
Production Editor: *Penelope Sky*
Manuscript Editor: *Lynne Y. Fletcher*
Permissions Editor: *May Clark*
Interior Design: *Laurie Albrecht*
Cover Design: *Katherine Minerva*
Associate Photo Editor: *Bob Western*
Typesetting: *Bookends Typesetting*
Printing and Binding: *Malloy Lithographing, Inc.*
Excerpts on page 61 and pages 102–105 appeared in the *Roanoke Times & World-News* on October 5, 1989.
Reprinted by permission of the Roanoke Times and World-News.

In Memory

I borrowed the title of this book from Professor Burton Blatt of Syracuse University. Among the many contributions he made to the field of mental retardation were two books, *Christmas in Purgatory* and *In and Out of Mental Retardation.*

Dr. Blatt was a bold and talented crusader for the rights of people with mental retardation. He was also an inspiration to a whole generation of scholars, teachers, and advocates. When he died in 1985 at the age of fifty-seven, professionals and people with disabilities everywhere mourned the loss of his great wisdom and compassion.

In writing this book I was deeply influenced by the life of Burton Blatt. Thank you for giving us a vision of the possible.

J. DAVID SMITH

University of South Carolina

A native of Roanoke, Virginia, J. David Smith earned his baccalaureate and master's degrees from Virginia Commonwealth University and his doctorate from Columbia University. He and his wife Joyce spent two years in Jamaica as Peace Corps volunteers. He has taught public school children with special needs and worked as a counselor. At Lynchburg College he taught counseling and special education courses and served as an associate dean. At the University of South Carolina, he is chair of the Department of Educational Psychology.

Dave is affiliated with a number of professional organizations, including the American Psychological Association and the Council for Exceptional Children, and has made presentations at numerous national conventions. The author of six previous books and many articles, Dave is also a licensed counselor.

Dave and Joyce, a kindergarten teacher, are the parents of three children. The whole family enjoys travel and cherishes the memory of camping from Virginia to Denali in Alaska in the magic summer of 1990.

Preface

No man is an Iland, intire of it self; every man is a piece of the continent, a part of the main.

—John Donne, *Devotions upon Emergent Occasions*

Historically, segregation has been a recurring social reaction to people who are considered to be defective or deficient in some way. We tend not to feel close to people we perceive as too different from the social norms and values we embrace. A society that believes that having a home is essential to normal human life will view homeless people as deviant, and it will distance them socially from its other members. A society that expects its members to be self-sufficient will look down on and isolate those who depend a great deal on others. A society that worships youth will revile old people. A society obsessed with physical and psychological perfection will seek ways to quarantine the imperfect.

This book is about the struggle of a socially imperfect person to connect with the society into which he was born but that has been reluctant to allow him to participate. It is a tale of a man who has spent a lifetime on isolated social shores. In his lonely existence he has rarely been touched, has often been ignored, and has regularly been avoided. He has been alone, his fears unarticulated and his frustrations unrecognized, for most of his life.

It is our own society that is involved in this story, the society of parents, friends, and teachers who encouraged us to be kind and generous to others, the society that nurtured us, instilled in us our values, and taught us how to behave. It is the society that continues to promote values that sometimes inspire us, sometimes challenge us, and sometimes tell us to look the other way when facing unsettling human differences or disturbing human need.

The isolated person, the metaphorical island in this story, is John Lovelace. He is in his sixties, and he is mentally retarded. I use his real name because I hope to reveal, not hide, a man who for most of his life has been socially invisible. I have wondered for some time what I should tell of this man and how I could best tell it. I remain fearful that something that I say about him could inadvertently hurt him, this person who has already known so much pain. I have concluded that I must tell the story of John Lovelace's lonely life in his own name. The risks of visibility are far less than the consequences of the isolation he has known.

Acknowledgments

The first word of thanks for help in preparing this book goes, as with all of my work, to Joyce Smith. She and our children, Link, Allison, and Sallie make my personal life a joy, and my life as a teacher and scholar possible.

I deeply appreciate the encouragement and friendship of Mary Bishop. She helped me greatly with this book and with my vision of people and the respect they deserve. She is a fine journalist and even finer person.

Mike Hudson greatly supported my concern for John Lovelace. He also made a valuable contribution to the welfare of people in the adult home system. He was sensitive and insightful in the way he first brought John Lovelace's story to the public.

A special acknowledgment is due to Vicki Knight, a wonderful editor and person. She believed in the importance of the story and made a commitment to reach as many readers as possible with its message.

My final acknowledgment is to John Lovelace. I respect his perseverance. I am glad to have him as my friend. I thank him for sharing his story with me.

J. David Smith

Contents

Introduction 1
1 "No Code": Do Not Resuscitate 7
2 "What Are You Going to Do About It?" 15
3 Etta Lovelace, Mrs. Hunter, and John 23
4 The No Code Is Rescinded 31
5 Patient 6839: Discharged to Zenia's Love 37
6 In and Out of an Institution 45
7 Deinstitutionalization 55
8 Smoking, Headaches, and Fights 65
9 Institutionalization, Sterilization, and Deinstitutionalization 73
10 John Lovelace and the Mercantile Theory of Mental Retardation 85
11 To: John Lovelace From: "Your Friends" 95
12 "Fairview Is Nice to Me" 107
13 Ethics, Powerlessness, and Informed Consent 115
14 Caring Friends, Blindness, and Pieces of Purgatory 125
15 Policies, People, and No Room in the Graveyard 135
Epilogue 143

Introduction

My Uncle Ganiel was the kind of man who made the world more interesting and exciting for a boy growing up in Virginia in the 1950s. He was a big man with a bold voice. He walked and talked with bravado, and he made me laugh. He kidded me in a way that I always knew expressed affection. Over the years he joked with me about girls, about remembering me as a toddler, about being too tall and skinny as an adolescent. He had rusty hair and freckles on his arms. He appeared strong against the world's stings, but I often saw his eyes fill with tears when he spoke of children in need. More than once I was aware that he bought groceries for a family in trouble. He had them delivered anonymously. From the time of my earliest recollections until he died I called him Uncle, just Uncle.

Uncle was a deer hunter. One of my early memories is of a deer head mounted on the wall of Uncle's living room. The antlers were shiny with shellac and the fur was stiff. But it was the brown glass eyes that were a source of amazement and intimidation to a four-year-old. They seemed to follow me wherever I walked, and I was afraid to stay alone in the room with the head. If Uncle was there, I felt safe.

Uncle owned a small hunting cabin. It was actually a house trailer that he had covered with a zinc roof and to which he had attached an addition. It was located on a few beautiful acres in a secluded forest area. Every fall Uncle went to his cabin during deer season for a few days. He would meet there with some of his friends and sometimes with his son, my cousin Orbie. One of his best friends had a cabin on an adjoining lot. It was a time for renewing and strengthening friendships, but I am not sure how much hunting was actually done.

Besides providing an opportunity to be with his friends, hunting was important to Uncle for another reason: It was a good excuse for having a dog. Over the years Uncle had a series of dogs that started out as working animals or strays and ended up as his beloved friends. Each seemed to have appeared out of a storm or to have been abandoned along an isolated road. Whatever the case, in each dog Uncle found a praiseworthy feature. His dog was always the smartest dog he had ever known, or the fastest dog he had ever seen, or the sweetest animal he had ever seen around children. The first of Uncle's dogs that I remember was Brownie. I have a vivid image of Brownie lying on the wide wooden porch that wrapped around the house that Uncle shared with my Aunt Catherine, Orbie, and my younger cousin Lisa. Brownie seemed to always be there sleeping in the sun while, as Uncle assured me, also doing his work of protecting the house. Actually, I don't think I ever heard Brownie bark at anyone or anything. Uncle once explained that Brownie was getting old and had already done his share of the world's work. He had, according to Uncle, been the best hunting dog he had ever seen. I always believed that Brownie was the dog that flushed the deer on Uncle's wall. Perhaps it was the only deer that either of them ever needed. I think the deer on the wall was a symbol of the bond between Uncle and Brownie that was complete in itself, requiring no further hunting.

I have wonderful memories of visits to Uncle's house as a child and teenager. Aunt Catherine always went out of her way to make me feel at home, Lisa was full of fun, and Orbie was inevitably involved in a project that fascinated me. He is a few years older than I and he taught me much about history, art, and philosophy through the model ships and planes that he constructed, the music he listened to, and the books that he talked about. Uncle always told me that I didn't eat "enough to keep a bird alive," but he also let me know that I didn't have to eat anything that I didn't want. Uncle himself had interesting dietary preferences. I don't remember a single lunch or dinner where Aunt Catherine didn't serve pinto beans. She once told me that Uncle had asked for pintos the first day they were married, and that since then she had always kept a pot of beans on the stove. She explained that he had grown up in a large family where pintos were the staple that enabled the family to be fed adequately day in and day out. Aunt Catherine usually also made mashed potatoes for every noon and evening meal. Fresh cornbread or white bread was common, and during the summer, sliced tomatoes and greenbeans rounded out the meals that I remember now with great pleasure.

Despite Uncle's apparent fondness for hunting—or at least for his cabin and his dogs—I do not remember ever seeing Uncle eat meat at lunch or dinner. Aunt Catherine explained to me that it was because meat had been so expensive and scarce in his family while he was growing up in rural poverty. Indeed, I remember once when Uncle came to our house one afternoon to pick up Aunt Catherine, who had been visiting with us for the morning. He had not had anything to eat since breakfast, yet he declined my mother's offers of leftover fried chicken. Instead, he took his own inventory of the contents of the refrigerator, and then proceeded to fix a sandwich of cold mashed potatoes on the heel slices from a loaf of bread. Watching Uncle eating a cold mashed potato sandwich made quite an impression on me.

Uncle was not a vegetarian. The first time I remember seeing him eat meat, however, was on an early morning in the pickup truck he used in his work for a hardware company. The night before, Uncle, Aunt Catherine, Orbie, Lisa, and I had squeezed into the truck cab for a ride to buy ice cream cones, and I left my hand in the hinge as the door was slammed shut. The pain was awful. I cried and felt panic. My fingernails immediately turned purple. Soon we were back in the house where Aunt Catherine carefully soaked and bandaged my fingers. Uncle paced and cussed at fate, at the truck, and perhaps even at himself. I knew, however, that his fury was not directed at me.

The next morning Uncle offered to give me another ride in his truck. I don't remember where Aunt Catherine, Orbie, and Lisa were but I do remember that Uncle and I, and Brownie, went for a ride. By this time Brownie was both blind and arthritic. Uncle had to help him into the truck. Soon Brownie was curled up on the floorboard. As we drove through the quiet streets of Roanoke, Uncle asked me if my fingers still hurt. He told me to be sure to keep soaking them regularly until the swelling, which was now very obvious, went down.

Uncle pulled the pickup into the parking lot of a diner that was a local legend. During the fifties and sixties, it sold hamburgers that were about the size of half dollars, for about fifteen cents each. For fifty cents you could buy four. In the mornings the same deal was offered for "sausageburgers." Uncle parked the truck, went into the diner, and soon returned with a bag. He insisted that I have two of the sandwiches. He had one. The fourth sausage sandwich he served to an appreciative Brownie on the floor of the truck's cab. Almost apologizing for giving the sandwich to a dog, Uncle told me that he thought it was important to remember that "an old dog like Brownie deserves to have a friend."

Uncle and Catherine lived modestly. They were not people who wasted things or indulged themselves, let alone a pet. Uncle wanted me to know that the sausageburger for Brownie was special. I will always remember that brief ride.

Uncle's last dog was named Benji. The two of them rode everywhere together in Uncle's car and were pretty much inseparable friends in all other respects. Among their rituals was an early-morning ride and a visit to the drive-thru at a local fast-food franchise. The days of the old diner and sausageburgers had, of course, given way to sausage biscuits at Hardee's. Because of Uncle's health problems, he himself could no longer eat sausage or the rich biscuits that the patties were served on. His trip to the drive-thru was just for Benji. Apparently, the workers at the Hardee's window looked forward each morning to seeing the dog sitting up with what they thought looked like a grin on his face in anticipation of his breakfast.

I once asked Uncle about Benji and his breakfast trips. He told me that it meant more to him to see his dog enjoying those sausage biscuits than if he were still able to eat them himself. He said that it was the same kind of feeling he got when he saw something good happening for one of his grandchildren—it felt better than if it were happening for him. "After a certain point in life," he said, "you have had enough of almost everything for yourself, and then the best times for you are when you see children and young people made happy by the little things you can do for them. And it's the same with Benji and his biscuits too." He added, "Of course, there has never been another dog quite like Benji."

I was a pallbearer at Uncle's funeral. I left for the funeral early and stopped for coffee at the Hardee's where Uncle and Benji had made their morning visits. I sat and thought of the years I had known Uncle and the good things he had done for me. He had made me feel important by giving me his attention, even through joking and kidding. He had taught me some important lessons about life by letting me see the sensitive and tender parts of his character. He had let me know that he was always glad to see me.

The eminent developmental psychologist Erik Erikson described four overarching tasks of adult life. These tasks that mark the lives of adults who have lived out their full potentials and possibilities include: the development of an independent sense of identity, the achievement of the capacity to be truly intimate and committed in relationships, and the ability to be wise and insightful about the temporary nature of one's own life and the achievement of peace concerning death. The fourth task of life that he considered critical to adult development is the development of the capacity for what he calls generativity. He used the term in part to describe the nurturing of a new generation as it is done by parents, and through which they discover new ways of caring for others. Through the experience of nurturing children, we may gain, for example, a new sense of the joy of giving and the meaningfulness of making sacrifices for those we love. Erikson felt, however, that we become generative not only with our own children but in the many ways that as adults we may care for extended families, neighbors, communities, churches, and other institutions.

My memories of Uncle exemplify for me what it means to be generative. His model of finding simple joy in the nurturance of others, even greater joy than in receiving rewards for himself, encourages me. I believe that this is the essence of being "grown up." Maturity means being more engaged in the growth and benefit of others who need your help than you are in your own gain. Erikson, in fact, described the opposite of generativity as self-absorption or stagnation. He felt that the adult who is unable to become generative becomes so self-focused that he or she is incapable of the joy of maturity. Such a person spends his or her time and energy seeking gratification for self, trying to ease the pain of a lonely existence.

Uncle's happiness at others' joy has also caused me to reflect upon our society as a whole. I have come to believe that we as a nation must recapture a sense of the generativity that earlier characterized our ideals. We as a nation must "grow up" enough again to look outward for the gratification of helping others to grow, to be healthier, to be more secure, to live better. The most fortunate among us have sought wealth, power, independence, and pleasure for ourselves and have found it. Now, if we are to be a truly generative nation, it is incumbent on us to face the poverty, homelessness, discouragement, and hopelessness in those all around us and find true gratification in helping others find nourishment, shelter, opportunities for growth, and belief in themselves. I dedicate what follows here to Uncle with the hope that a spirit of generativity will again come alive in our culture.

Chapter 1

"No Code": Do Not Resuscitate

Professors have been accused of leading lives detached from the daily realities of the very world they study and teach about. This accusation is true in some respects. The only way to see an intellectual, artistic, or social vista is to stand back and look at the people, events, and objects that constitute the landscape from a distance. Having spent most of my working life as a college and university professor, I have had the privilege of doing just this.

The work of standing back and observing the changing cultural horizon contrasts sharply with my earlier experiences as a public school teacher, a counselor, and a Peace Corps volunteer. My present position is also far removed from the intense and challenging work with people with handicaps that I did while in high school and college. Besides enabling me to finance my schooling, that work in summer camps, treatment centers, and hospitals also called me to something more than a way to make a living: It gave me a vocation. At places with names like Camp Easter Seal, the Virginia Treatment Center for Children, and the Virginia Home, I learned that I could make a direct and positive difference in the lives of people who needed help. I also learned that I enjoyed making a difference.

While my wife, Joyce, and I were serving in the Peace Corps in Jamaica, I discovered that I was pulled to another kind of work—assisting people who would in turn help others, thereby amplifying my efforts. My work with the Ministry of Education in Jamaica fostered in me a sense of the importance of helping teachers, prospective teachers, counselors, and other helping professionals become as competent at and committed to improving the quality of life for others as possible. During the two years that we served in Jamaica, I came to believe that my work in life should somehow involve helping people to help others.

Living in Jamaica taught me something else as well. While training for that commitment, we were told that one of the most difficult aspects of our service in Jamaica would come after we returned to the United States. We were advised that most people would have difficulty seeing beyond the stereotype of Jamaica as a tropical paradise and understanding why the Peace Corps was needed there. Indeed, since our return from Jamaica in 1971, many have asked how we "lucked out," and whether we enjoyed the limbo dances and scuba diving; some have even commented that the rum punch hangovers must have been hell. Living amid the beauty of that struggling island nation's landscape, people, and customs did, indeed, have its pleasures. But Jamaica was also, at the time, one of the poorest nations in the Western Hemisphere, and it continues to battle for its economic survival and its social integrity in the world community. I learned much, living there, about how little we in the United States understand about the lives of most people in the world that surrounds us. Joyce and I came home having rarely glimpsed the resorts that dominate the American image of the country we had come to love for its sense of pride, purpose, and dignity. We also came back with a deeper sense of the complexity of the social world in which we all live and the difficulty of defining one's place in it.

The Peace Corps, Jamaica, graduate school, beginning my career as a professor—all of these life markers are part of my history now. For nineteen years, first at Lynchburg College in Virginia and now at the University of South Carolina, I have been teaching people who are preparing to become teachers or counselors, or who are otherwise interested in special education, rehabilitation, and counseling. In that span, I have also become part of the establishment. I am a vested member of the professoriate and am concerned about all of the practical matters that concern any worker: working conditions, salary, security. My identity, however, is intimately tied to being an effective teacher, a competent scholar, and a good citizen of my professional community. I continue to think that I made the right decision in choosing to try to help those who would in turn help others. I must admit, however, that the nature of my work does separate me from the people who are my subject: children and adults with exceptional needs, with handicaps, with disabilities. Though I do not believe that my academic tower is so high or unapproachable, I must admit that I live and thrive there. I only hope that what I do there is ultimately useful.

I do have several anchors in the "real world" that I think ensure that ivy doesn't overgrow my perceptions of reality. I work voluntarily with several programs that bring me into regular contact with children and adults with disabilities. I also frequently visit teachers and other human-service providers at their places of work. These anchors remind me of how difficult helping people who most need help can be. They also remind me of how life enhancing that work can be.

My strongest anchor for many years was a weekend camp that some of my Lynchburg College students and I shared each semester with people who are mentally retarded. Each November and April, fifty students planned and staffed a camp for a group of about fifty mentally retarded children and adults. There were always new faces among the campers, but we also had a group of "regulars." The same was true of the college students. Those students who had participated before and knew what to expect would help the newcomers with their natural anxieties.

The facility we used for the weekend, Camp Virginia Jaycee, is operated by the Jaycees during the summer and serves about a thousand children and adults from Virginia who are mentally retarded. Seventeen years ago, the executive director of the camp, Ev Werness, and I began the collaboration that resulted in these off-season camping weekends.

The Camp Jaycee weekends became a tradition at Lynchburg College. As it evolved, the camp became a campuswide activity, not one solely for special education majors. Throughout the year I would run into students on campus whose conversation always focused on the next camp weekend. More students majoring in other fields took part each year. To see a business major or a communications major helping an intimidated twelve-year-old throw a ball or tying the shoes of a sixty-year-old man who couldn't do it for himself was extremely gratifying. It was even more gratifying to realize that these acts were performed in every instance freely, gladly, and with no reward other than the satisfaction intrinsic in sharing in a genuine human exchange. I always returned from those three days feeling good about the interaction I had observed between fifty bright young college students with a world of options open to them and fifty people whose options were limited by the life circumstances they had been dealt. I also felt privileged to have witnessed what I believe is the best of what this generation of college students has to offer. Contrary to some reports, they promise to bring much to be valued to their future and ours.

I returned from the Camp Jaycee weekend in April 1987 feeling, as usual, warm and optimistic. I was also extremely troubled. The event that had disturbed and challenged me was the same one that introduced me to John Lovelace and that would lead me to become involved in his life. That event, that weekend, fundamentally changed me, and, I believe, it changed John's life in at least some minimal ways.

The student staffers and I always left for Camp Jaycee early on Friday afternoon, arriving at the camp, set in a beautiful valley at the foot of the Blue Ridge Mountains, around two o'clock. After making cabin assignments and unpacking, the students, who were now beginning to think of themselves as counselors, would gather in the camp dining hall. After a few words of orientation from me, they would meet in groups to go over the application materials of the campers assigned to their cabins, who would begin arriving at four o'clock. Included in each application was information on the camper's medications, level of retardation, and special needs or precautions.

In April 1987, as Ev Werness was handing out the materials to each group, he approached me with a file and a question. Among the papers for John Lovelace was a medical consultation form—which I now believe was included by mistake. Even more disturbing, however, is the possibility that no one thought twice about including it.

John was fifty-six years old that spring and living in a large adult home in nearby Roanoke. The Burrell Home for Adults housed close to two hundred people—people whom someone familiar with many of their situations later described to me as "dead-end" people. They were mostly poor, sick, old, severely handicapped, alone in life, or some combination thereof. The building itself is a tragic anachronism. In the fifties, it had been the segregated hospital for black people in the area.

In the eighties, it was still an instrument of segregation, its residents pariahs now not because of race but because they could claim no other place in a society in which they were only marginal members.

The consultation form attached to John Lovelace's application was dated a week before the camp weekend. It included the following notes:

A. Vascular anomaly
B. 1. Not a surgical candidate
   2. No code
   3. . . . Do not resuscitate in the event of cardiac arrest.

Ev showed me the form and asked what I thought it meant for John's weekend stay at Camp Jaycee. I was immediately disturbed by the larger implications of the words on the form but narrowed my focus to respond to Ev's immediate concern. We discussed it briefly and quickly agreed that we could not consider it a valid directive for the weekend. We decided that if there were a medical crisis involving John, we would seek the same emergency treatment for him that we would for anyone else. We shared this decision with the nurse who had been employed for the weekend and agreed that in a major emergency of any kind every life-sustaining measure would be used.

Two other notations on the form struck me as important: that John had no next of kin and that John "maintains his own personal affairs." These notations led me to suspect that John had been asked to agree to the no-code order—that he had been treated as a competent adult with no need of a guardian or other advocate. This hunch later proved correct.

Friday evening at Camp Jaycee was always interesting. The main event was a dance that always got even the most timid camper and nervous college student out on the floor. It was so much fun that everything else was lost in the music and movement. For a while, I almost forgot about the no-code order. John Lovelace himself danced much of the night away with several of the counselors assigned to his cabin.

After the dance was over and the campers were in bed, the students gathered as usual in the dining hall to talk about the events of the past few hours. This is always a period of emotional release, with students who had had doubts earlier in the day finding new self-confidence and asking a torrent of questions about the campers: Why does he do this? Why is she afraid of that? Do you think that she understands? What should I do if . . . ? Often, questions come up that I can't answer to the satisfaction of my students. One of these arose that night in April 1987.

I had spoken with a few of the students earlier about John and the no-code order. They had talked with others, and now there was general interest in knowing more about both. I talked about the meaning of a no-code order—no treatment to sustain life in a threatening physical crisis—and the reasons for such an order—the quality of the person's life does not justify saving it. We compared John with other people who might be under a no-code order—someone in a continuing coma, for instance, or someone with a degenerative disease who suffers continual, severe, irremediable pain. John just did not fit with these cases. He is mentally retarded, but his condition is not degenerative. He has intellectual and social handicaps, but he is responsive to his environment. John is ambulatory, he is not chronically ill, and he seems to derive pleasure from life when given the opportunity.

The students wanted to know why John had been "written off." I could only guess. John is not only mentally retarded but also poor and alone in life; he has no advocate to speak for him or to assert his value as a person; and he is likely to be viewed by some as a "surplus person," a noncontributing member of society. These factors taken together make him an unlikely candidate for extraordinary care and treatment: John is expendable. I took this opportunity to emphasize to the students that the failure to recognize people who are mentally retarded as fully human is not confined to a dim and uninformed institutional past. The struggle for human rights for people who are handicapped continues today, and I concluded my comments by encouraging the students to be a part of that struggle.

At that point, I was feeling good about what I had said and was even glad that John's plight had come to our attention. It had, after all, proved a gripping lesson for all of us.

Then came *the* question. I was prepared for questions about mental retardation or about social and medical ethics. The question that came, however, cut straight to the fabric of my own values and ethics. It came from a student who for several months had been listening to me speak in class of the critical need for advocacy and activism on behalf of people who are disabled. At the end of my commentary on John Lovelace, she looked me straight in the eyes and, with trust and sincerity, asked, "Dr. Smith, what are you going to do about it?"

I'm sure the question was not meant as a challenge; it was the question of a concerned twenty-year-old who believed that I could make a difference. The directness and sincerity of her trust shook me. I was also intimidated by the assumption that I was both committed to and capable of doing something that would make some kind of meaningful difference for John.

How I wished that I had some bold and definitive plan to tell my student. In fact, I had nothing to offer. The best I could do was say that I wasn't sure yet just what could be done, if anything. I then mumbled something about having to be careful with confidential information and about not wanting to do anything that would hurt other campers' chances of coming to our weekends. I closed by saying I would look further into the matter.

The rest of the weekend went well. All of the students, particularly those in his cabin, paid special attention to John. He responded with appreciation and what seemed to be caution. There were no further questions from the students about John and his future. In their untutored wisdom, they simply related to him as a human being who deserved dignity and compassion.

We returned to Lynchburg College exhausted but gratified. Inside me, however, the question kept echoing: "Dr. Smith, what are you going to do about it?"

Chapter 2

"What Are You Going to Do About It?"

"What are you going to do about it?"

Earlier that same year, my seven-year-old daughter, Allison, had asked me the same question. We were on vacation in New York City. Joyce and I had looked forward for some time to introducing our three children to the city. We had lived there while studying and working at Columbia University, and we had treasured memories that we wanted to revisit and share with Link, Allison, and Sallie.

In the decade since we had lived there, however, New York City had been faced with greater challenges than ever before. Changes in federal policies and programs had manifested themselves most visibly among the urban poor. There were more homeless, confused, and disenfranchised people on the streets of New York than we had ever seen. My children had learned the term *street people* as an abstraction. Now, as we walked the streets of the city, they connected that term with the real people they saw sleeping on the pavement, rummaging through garbage, or walking about disoriented and clearly impoverished.

Allison, in particular, was moved by what she saw, and asked if I thought that one man, who looked alarmingly dirty, ill, and exhausted, would die. I answered that unless something happened—unless he got help—he probably would. That was when she asked what I have come to call "Allison's question."

Joyce and I, like most parents, are trying to teach our children to do the "right thing" in relation to other people. Again like most other parents, we try to teach our children at least partially by example, modeling, we hope, how to treat other people with care and respect. So I understand that Allison's question was a positive sign: She had come to expect her mother and me to try to help people who need it. At seven, however, she also believed that we had the ability to do whatever needed to be done.

On the street in New York, I was as inarticulate answering Allison's question as I was to be answering my student's about John Lovelace. As I stumbled and stammered my way around Allison's concern, the best I could do was talk about not being able to help everyone in need and about how our contributions to church and charities help people like the man she was so concerned about. She was not satisfied with the answer. I was embarrassed to have offered it to my child. The moment passed, but my discomfort did not.

In the biblical story of the Good Samaritan, the two men who passed by the sufferer without helping him crossed to the other side of the road as they passed. Not only would they not help, they did not want to be near the suffering. These men were probably not unfeeling and inhumane. They simply would not risk becoming involved. Perhaps they were family men with responsibilities to others that took precedence. Perhaps they were afraid of being tricked and finding themselves victims of attack and robbery, or of becoming involved with someone who would require more and more of them. And so, they walked to the other side of the road to avoid seeing the hurting man whom they felt they could not help.

It was months before I spoke with Allison again about her question. I was finally able to talk with her about the limits to what one person can do in helping others. In addition, recalling the parable of the Good Samaritan, I explained to Allison that though her mother and I cannot help everyone who needs help, we do care. I promised her that though seeing a need one cannot meet is painful, we will always look at others and their needs, and care about them. I explained that what is most important is that we not walk to the other side of the road. We talked, and I believe she understood what I was trying to say.

I came close to telling my students the same thing in regard to John Lovelace: that we could do nothing about John's situation but that we could—should—be sensitized by our knowledge of it. Just knowing of the no-code decision in John's case, I thought, could make us more aware of our society's devaluing of the lives of people who are mentally retarded and inspire us to make a difference when and where we could. I came close to leaving it at that.

Please understand that nowhere in this story should my efforts on John's behalf be considered extraordinary. There is only one hero in this story: John Lovelace, who is heroic in his psychological and social survival. I have done nothing heroic here at all.

The philosopher Judith Jarvis Thomson, in discussing the murder of Kitty Genovese decades ago in New York City, revisited the story of the Good Samaritan. You may recall that Kitty Genovese was murdered—repeatedly attacked—while thirty-eight people watched from their apartments and did nothing to help her. Thomson said that a Good Samaritan would have rushed out, risking death in an attempt to help. Such a person, she said, would be not just good but a Splendid Samaritan! In fact, however, not one of the thirty-eight witnesses even picked up a telephone to call the police, an action that would have caused them no danger. Calling the police, Thomson said, would have been the act of a Minimally Decent Samaritan. What we need to make a decent society is not a few Splendid Samaritans but millions of Minimally Decent Samaritans.

The confidence and trust of that twenty-year-old student proved too much for me to allow John's story to be just an example cited in a lecture. I decided to at least step a little closer to John's life, even if it meant seeing a hurt more clearly and still being unable to help. I decided to make what I thought would be a minimally decent inquiry on his behalf. On Monday morning, I wrote to the Burrell Home, where John was living, addressing my letter to the social worker who had arranged for John to come to Camp Jaycee. From her comments in the records I'd seen at camp, she appeared to take a personal interest in him. I wrote to her as follows:

> First let me introduce myself. I am a professor at Lynchburg College. Each semester I take a group of students to Camp Virginia

Jaycee for a weekend. These students, special education majors, nursing majors, and others who are interested, serve as counselors for the respite weekends of which you are aware. I have been taking students to Camp Virginia Jaycee for more than a decade.

This past weekend some information which puzzles me concerning one of your residents who attended the camping weekend came to my attention. Included with the information on John Lovelace was a medical consultation form. The date of the consultation was 3/24/87. The consultation appears to have been a followup on John's recent illness with flu. Under the heading of "Recommendations" are the following statements:

A. Vascular anomaly
B. 1. Not a surgical candidate
   2. No code
   3. Tinker Mountain [a sheltered workshop]
      Do not resuscitate in the event of cardiac arrest.

I find these statements most disturbing. I am asking for your help in understanding these recommendations. I noticed on the consultation form that John has no next of kin. I assume that you are the person who knows most about him. That is why I am writing to you for help in understanding this matter. Will you help me with this?

Thanks in advance for your assistance. Please let me know if you have any questions.

The next Thursday, April 7, I received a call from John's social worker. She was pleasant and as helpful as she could be, given the conditions of our conversation: Confidentiality concerns strictly limited what she could discuss with me. I had no right by way of kinship or legal authority to information concerning John, so there was little that she could discuss with me. She was able to confirm my hunch that even though John had spent many years in a mental retardation institution, he had never been declared incompetent and, therefore, had never been assigned a legal guardian of any sort. Though unable to discuss it, she also confirmed for me that John had participated in the no-code decision as a legally competent party. I asked her if the vascular anomaly mentioned on the consultation form was an uncorrectable condition that could potentially create a life-threatening crisis. She could not comment on this in any detail but shared my impression that this was the case.

The only way to look into John's situation more closely appeared to be with legal assistance. The Virginia Department for the Rights of the Disabled seemed to me to be a good place to start.

Later that same day, I wrote to Susan Spielberg of the Department for the Rights of the Disabled:

> Dear Ms. Spielberg:
>
> I attended the session that you and your associates conducted at Virginia Tech in September and was most impressed. I now have the need to call upon your expertise in a more direct manner.
>
> The enclosed copy of a letter I wrote recently will indicate to you that I am concerned for the well-being of a 56-year-old mentally retarded man. The information I cite in the letter to his social worker will indicate to you that I am concerned as to whether the best interests of John Lovelace are being protected. By the way, John is completely ambulatory, has all the basic self-help skills, and thoroughly enjoyed the camping weekend I refer to in the letter. . . .
>
> I received a call this morning from [the social worker] which was most helpful. Although our conversation was limited by the confidentiality of the matter, she explained to me that John has never been declared incompetent and, therefore, does not have a legal guardian. Because of his circumstance, John apparently participated in the "no code" decision. I would question whether he is actually capable of a decision of that magnitude. [She] did indicate that his vascular condition is considered to be inoperable.
>
> I would appreciate hearing from you with any opinions or advice you may have to offer. Thanks very much for considering my request. Please let me know if you have any questions.

Susan responded promptly to my request for assistance, expressing agreement with my concern over John's ability to give informed consent in a matter of such gravity and indicating that she had already assigned a staff attorney to assist me in exploring the matter.

The attorney soon contacted me, and after we discussed the case briefly, she gave me an assignment. She would send the appropriate consent forms to me and I would take them to Roanoke, have John sign them, and see that they were returned to her. She would then start the process of obtaining the records that would tell us more about John's circumstances. She also asked for the names and addresses of persons from whom the necessary records could be requested.

On the first Monday in May, I wrote her explaining:

> I visited John Lovelace at the Burrell Home for Adults in Roanoke yesterday. I read the consent form to him and explained it as best I could. He signed it with no hesitation. He executed his signature with great effort and care. It is not very clear but it is genuinely his and I expect is typical of the way he signs his name.
>
> I hope that you will find the form to be in proper order and ready to use. I am anxious to see what John's records can tell us. It seems to me that the basic questions we should be seeking to answer at this point are:
>
> 1. What is the exact nature of John's "vascular anomaly"? What is the usual correction for this condition? Why has John's condition not been treated?
> 2. Why is John "not a surgical candidate"? What is the significance of his mental retardation in being so designated? What is the significance of his financial situation in this designation? Did his having "no next of kin" influence this decision?
> 3. How was the "no code—do not resuscitate" decision made? Did John participate in the decision? Is he truly competent to make such a decision? Is this decision actually in his best interest?
>
> These are the kinds of questions which have been driving my concern for John's welfare. I offer them to you for refinement in relation to the legal structure. I look forward to your opinions on these matters.

I followed this letter with another suggesting possible sources of information for the attorney to pursue. I recommended that she contact the physician who issued the no-code order and, of course, the adult home where he had been living. I also suggested that she try the Mental Health and Mental Retardation Services office in Roanoke. By this time I had located and spoken with the social worker who had worked with John when he had lived at what was now called the Central Virginia Training Center. She seemed to remember John well. I felt that, released from confidentiality constraints by the consent form, she could probably provide important insights on what John's life had been like while he was in the institution, which might in turn help illuminate his present situation. Soon after passing this information on to the attorney, however, I felt a growing need to know more about John's life for myself, and I began my own search to retrieve his history for both of us—for him because he is entitled to a heritage, for me because I needed to understand how a human life can come to be so devalued by its own society.

Chapter 3

Etta Lovelace, Mrs. Hunter, and John

On May 26, 1931, a young woman was officially committed to Western State Hospital in Staunton, Virginia—though she was not retained in the institution at that time. She was, to use the institutional term, "furloughed" until the legal paperwork could be completed for the procedure that was the real reason for her commitment. The nineteen-year-old was to have surgery under Virginia's involuntary sterilization law, declared constitutional by the United States Supreme Court in 1927, in the case of *Buck* v. *Bell.* The law allowed the state to sterilize people found to be incompetent because of (to again use some of the terms of the time) feeblemindedness, insanity, alcoholism, epilepsy, prostitution, and the like.

The young woman's name was Etta Virginia Lovelace. According to the commitment papers, hospitalization at Western State, a psychiatric institution, was necessary because of "immoral conduct and sexual promiscuity." Her records also indicate that she had one illegitimate child. She was described as having been "feebleminded since birth; mother and father were also feebleminded." There was no elaboration of or substantiation for these diagnoses.

On June 29, 1931, Etta Lovelace was returned to the hospital from furlough in preparation for her sterilization. Apparently, the necessary legal documents had been processed by that time. It was noted that she adjusted well to the hospital routine and "helped a great deal on the ward." Her hospital records indicate that she was sterilized on November 1, 1931, and "made an uneventful post-operative recovery."

Etta Lovelace was to live in the institution for almost another two years. The hospital records do not indicate any reason for her being held that long. My sense is that she was held simply because the large state hospital bureaucracy operated so slowly. Apparently, during those two years no psychological testing was done that might have supported the legitimacy of her diagnosis as feebleminded. Notes under the heading "Formal Mental Examination" offer some insight into this young woman's character, however:

> She was cooperative and attentive. Answered questions to the best of her ability. She gave a history of having had one illegitimate child which had been taken from her by a minister in her community. She did not object to the operation for sterilization. She was able to do simple counting and calculation, but was unable to read, but could write her name. She had worked successfully as a housekeeper in various homes prior to admission. She had been arrested on one occasion for vagrancy. She said that this was due to her inability to get a job where she could stay in the house, and she had no place to go.

Apparently, Etta Lovelace was diagnosed as feebleminded because she could not read, had an illegitimate child, and was poor. The records indicate that she was "unimproved" at her discharge. Her formal diagnosis was "Without psychosis, Mental deficiency, Moron."

Moron was the term used at the time for "high-grade defectives," individuals judged to be mentally retarded but who showed no clear signs of head injury, malformation, or disease. They were thought to be retarded because of genetic weakness—the product of "poor stock" or "bad seed," with insufficient intelligence to cope with normal social demands. They were also thought to be highly prone to crime, immorality, and promiscuity. Much of the expansion in number and size of residential institutions and the implementation of involuntary sterilization practices during the first half of this century was aimed at this group. Even a brief study of what occurred in the field of mental retardation during this period, however, reveals that those who were diagnosed as morons, then institutionalized and sterilized, were poor, uneducated people who, for one reason or another, were considered social misfits by those in positions of authority. The men and women who were institutionalized and sterilized tended to have neither advocates to help them nor the resources to help themselves. Etta Lovelace fits this profile perfectly.

In the physical examination given when she was admitted to Western State Hospital, Etta was described as being 5 feet, 6 inches tall and weighing 140 pounds. She had brown hair and blue eyes. Her health was good, but her socially unacceptable behavior made her a problem. She was poor and uneducated. She had no advocates. When interviewed upon admission to the hospital, she stated that she made her living doing housework.

> *What did you do in the house?* Cleaned up and cooked, and washed. *What did you cook?* Anything I could get hold of. *Can you cook beans?* Yes. *How?* Wash them nice and clean, and put water and salt and a piece of meat in them. *How long does it take to cook them?* I put them on at nine o'clock and they are done by 10. . . . *Can you make biscuits?* Yes. *How?* Cut them out. *What do you put in them?* Soda, sometimes baking powders, and milk. *What sort of milk?* Butter milk. . . . *How do you make corn bread?* I take two eggs and milk and a little soda and salt. *What do you do besides cooking?* Nothing but work on the farm. I shucked corn and suckered tobacco. . . . *Did you ever have any children?* One. *Is it alive?* Yes. . . . *How old is the baby?* It was born last year at the time we shucked corn. *Who is looking after the child?* A preacher took him away from me. *Do you nurse the baby?* Feed him on the bottle. *You have just had one?* Yes. *Were you willing to come and stay here for us to help you and do what we can for you?* I would rather stay at home.

And so the story of John Lovelace's life begins to take form. He was born to Etta in 1930 but was soon taken from her. She was then institutionalized and sterilized. After two years, she would return to her home in Martinsville, Virginia, but she would never reestablish a maternal relationship with her son. He would subsequently know about her, but he would never know her as his mother.

A 1946 physician's report sheds some light on John's early life after he was taken from his mother:

> The Salvation Army was looking for a temporary home in which to place the child. They placed the baby with this family and never made arrangements to take him out. Consequently, he has been with them without adoption all of his life. They have treated him as their own child. The foster-mother had been married before and had a daughter, who now has children. When the child was six months old his eyes and mouth drew over to the right, and he had "drawing" spells, in which his head and heels almost touched. These would last for an hour or more. They continued for two weeks. He was taken to Dr. Newman in Danville, who determined that he had syphilis and treated him. This helped a great deal, but the boy has never been right. They put him in school, and the teacher frankly told the foster-mother that he couldn't learn. The foster-mother tried to teach him herself, but she found out that it was impossible.

When John was sixteen, his foster parents became concerned about some peculiarities in his behavior. Most troubling were his temper tantrums. The same physician outlined the foster parents' worries:

> The main concern now is that during the past year he has had an increase in his rages. They have become more violent. He is very cruel to the animals, and on one occasion he attacked his foster-mother with a pitchfork and a knife. He has had periods when he eats ravenously, and then periods when he will go without anything. He has begun to masturbate. He will play well with the foster-mother's grandchildren for several hours and then will become irritated with them. He will have periods of being fractious, and if his foster-mother does not appear to pay attention to them, they disappear and he seems to repent. He makes a great deal of noise sleeping.

Some of these characteristics are not unusual in a sixteen-year-old boy. Others indicate a frustrated young man in turmoil. The physician

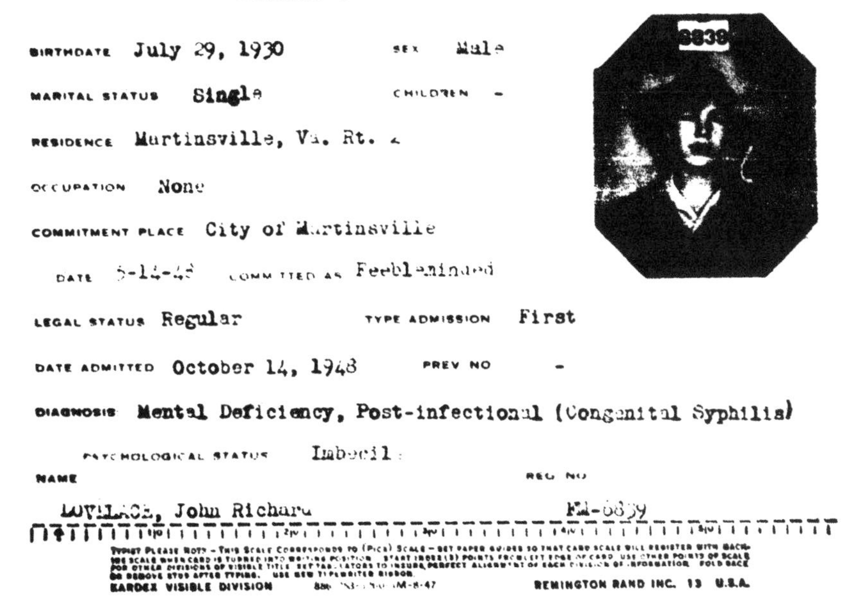

LYNCHBURG STATE COLONY

BIRTHDATE July 29, 1930 SEX Male

MARITAL STATUS Single CHILDREN -

RESIDENCE Martinsville, Va. Rt. [illegible]

OCCUPATION None

COMMITMENT PLACE City of Martinsville

DATE 5-14-48 COMMITTED AS Feebleminded

LEGAL STATUS Regular TYPE ADMISSION First

DATE ADMITTED October 14, 1948 PREV NO -

DIAGNOSIS Mental Deficiency, Post-infectional (Congenital Syphilis)

PSYCHOLOGICAL STATUS Imbecile

NAME REG NO

LOVELACE, John Richard FM-6839

KARDEX VISIBLE DIVISION REMINGTON RAND INC. 13 U.S.A.

Photocopy of the record of John Lovelace's admission to the Virginia Colony for the Feebleminded and Epileptics, in Lynchburg, Virginia, on October 14, 1948.

went on to describe John's physical disabilities and apparent mental handicap. He said that John walked with a limp on his right side. His speech was impaired, his mental abilities appeared limited, and his reflexes were slow.

Among John's "virtues" were being "good at milking" and at working in the family's garden. He apparently was also helpful in other ways on the farm.

John's difficulties continued to overshadow his virtues. Two years later, at age eighteen, he was institutionalized, committed to what was commonly known as the Lynchburg State Colony. Its official title was the Virginia Colony for the Feebleminded and Epileptics. Since called the Lynchburg Training School and Hospital and, most recently, the Central Virginia Training Center, it has for many years been the largest residential facility in the United States for people diagnosed as mentally retarded. The *Buck* v. *Bell* sterilization case was initiated here and it was here that Carrie Buck was sterilized following the Supreme Court's 1927 decision.

John was committed in October 1948. As part of that process, a social worker from Martinsville wrote to a social worker at the Colony about John's home life. Her comments reveal much about the atmosphere in which John had grown up, as well as providing more detail about the difficulties he had been having. Her comments also indicate that John had been legally adopted. I have found no records to confirm that this is true.

> We talked with Mr. and Mrs. W. I. Hunter, foster parents of the above named child. The Hunters live in a very cheap mill section and have a very small home. The house is very sparsely furnished, but immaculately kept. It was rather early in the morning when the worker called, but even at that hour the house was spotless, as well as Mr. and Mrs. Hunter and John. Both the parents gave the worker the impression of being honest and sincere.
>
> Mr. and Mrs. Hunter were attending a Salvation Army meeting about eighteen years ago and were asked to take a baby and keep it for ten days until a permanent home could be found. They kept the child for almost a year before they legally adopted him. When they took the baby, all they knew about his background was that his mother was unmarried. Later they found that she was not normal mentally. Since then they have also met several of his aunts and from what they say, feeblemindedness is a strong family characteristic. The child was taken to Dr. Newman, Pediatrician, Danville, Virginia, who gave him shots for syphilis. When John was six months old he had infantile paralysis. This affected his right side. He was almost four years old before he began to talk or walk. Over the period of eighteen years, the Hunters have carried John from first one doctor to another, with the hope that something might be done for him.
>
> In 1945 he was examined at the University of Virginia Hospital, Charlottesville, Virginia. For the last three or four weeks the boy has been having a very severe headache every day. These headaches lasted for a very short while. It seems that John is very calm and harmless until his blood pressure goes up. Mrs. Hunter says that

> when this happens he becomes very angry and seems to want to hurt something.

The social worker's statement portrays a caring couple with limited resources who gave much to a child in desperate need of acceptance and care. It also shows that they had reached the limits of their abilities to help and understand him. In 1948 there was no help available to them outside the institution to which they sent their son. There was simply nowhere else for them to turn for assistance.

Also evident are the conflict and bias that would continue regarding the reason for John's disabilities. Congenital syphilis was again mentioned. Polio (infantile paralysis) is introduced as a reason for physical limitations on the right side of his body. Finally, his genetic heritage is questioned, with his mother's and her sisters' "feeblemindedness" advanced as an explanation for John's difficulties. Each of these explanations was to be cited again and again as John moved in and out of the social institutions that controlled his destiny.

In October 1948, John Richard Lovelace became Patient 6839 at the state colony. On John's fourth day in residence there, a psychologist evaluated him, concluding his report with the following observations.

> Despite the fact that the family from which he is derived is filled with incidence of mental deficiency, it appears that the diagnosis will have to be a toss-up between birth injury or congenital lues [congenital syphilis].
>
> *Recommendation:* Sterilization seems to be feasible since his foster-parents are anxious for him to be furloughed for short periods of time. He is given to too much agitation and is too low grade to profit from any school. Simple training in manual tasks combined with recreational therapy are about all that can be offered.

Chapter 4

The "No Code" Is Rescinded

On May 29, 1987, the attorney with the Virginia Department for the Rights of the Disabled who was assisting me in my inquiry into the "no-code" order issued for John Lovelace contacted the physician who had written the order. In her letter, she expressed my concern over whether John was really able to understand the full meaning of such a decision—that is, whether he was capable of giving informed consent for the order. Her wording was consistent with my assumption that John had never been declared incompetent and, therefore, may not have been helped with the decision by a guardian or advocate. After delineating my concerns to the physician, she asked that he explain the circumstances surrounding the decision and the nature of John's health problems. She also asked that he send copies of John's medical records for the last two years. She enclosed a copy of the release form that John had signed for me a few weeks earlier granting us access to his records.

Just over a month later, the attorney let me know that she had not heard from the physician or the adult home where John was living. To my disappointment, this interested and able attorney also informed me that she had resigned her position and that my case would be reassigned in a few weeks. In fact, in the course of trying to learn about John Lovelace, I discovered that legal aid services like the Virginia Department for the Rights of the Disabled seem to have trouble recruiting and maintaining lawyers of her caliber. Even though the agency seemed to be doing its best to address my concern, it took three attorneys and more than a year to get my questions about John answered.

The second attorney seemed suspicious of my motives for getting involved in John's life. He also questioned the appropriateness of my concern about John's ability to make a life-and-death decision when "advocates like yourself," as he said, had been battling in recent years for the right of disabled people to make more of their own decisions. I later learned that he had actually received a reply from the physician involved in the case by the end of July, though when I called him, he said that he was still investigating and would anyway be unable to discuss any findings with me until I had obtained additional release forms signed by John and two witnesses. I secured the releases, sent them to the attorney, and waited for a reply. No word came. I wrote in September asking to be advised on the progress of the case. I received no reply. I wrote again in October, and again in November. In January 1988, I was informed that this lawyer had left the agency and that my case had been assigned to yet another attorney.

John Gifford, my third attorney, pursued the matter aggressively and competently. He kept me informed of his actions and their results. He has my thanks and respect. On January 19, he sent me a copy of what the previous attorney had received in July—a letter from John's physician explaining the case and his actions. The physician said that because John had been having severe headaches, a CT (computed tomography) scan of the head had been ordered. The scan revealed an infarction in the brain. A neurosurgeon who was then consulted declared that John's disabilities did not make him a candidate for surgery. The letter continued:

> In March of 1987, Mr. Lovelace became more lethargic and I became more concerned about our course of action if he were to sustain a cardiac or respiratory arrest. I then attempted to locate any relatives or next of kin to discuss this situation. However, I was informed that there was no record of any next of kin and that Mr. Lovelace was handling his affairs (See document #3). I discussed with Mr. Lovelace his medical condition, the CT scan report, and [the neurosurgeon's report]. I then asked his desires in the event of cardiac or pulmonary arrest and the maintenance of life systems following such. Mr. Lovelace indicated to me that he did not

> want resuscitative measures in case of cardio-pulmonary arrest. I concurred and indicated on 3-24-87, to the Burrell Home for Adults, his "no code" status (See document #4). If questions remain regarding Mr. Lovelace and these steps, please communicate with me.

My immediate response as I read that final comment was rage and confusion. How could this letter have been sitting on a lawyer's desk or in his files for six months without my even having been informed that the inquiry was progressing? How could what appeared to me to be a glaring inconsistency have remained unquestioned? The no-code order was written March 24, 1987, based in part on the fact that John had no next of kin. The documentation for that fact (Document #3), however, was dated March 25, 1987. It reads as follows:

> Per your request, this is confirmation that we have no record of John Lovelace having any next of kin. I have also taken the liberty to see if Mental Health Services had any such records and they also have no record of any next of kin.

The social worker who wrote this letter had gone beyond what had been requested of her by checking a source outside the adult home for possible information on John's relatives. Still, the search was certainly not vigorous. Most glaring, however, is that the order was issued the day *before* there was any documentation of there being no next of kin on record.

Before I contacted John Gifford about this issue, however, he called me with even more startling news. John was no longer living in the adult home in Roanoke. Because of concerns about his increasing behavior problems, he had been transferred temporarily to a psychiatric rehabilitation center. There it had been determined that his placement in the adult home was no longer appropriate for him, and he had been discharged. He had then been moved to a small adult home in a rural area just outside of Roanoke. The dynamics of that move remain a puzzle to me. I still don't know whether John was discharged because of a real worsening in his behavior at the home or whether my "meddling" caused him to be perceived as a problem to be gotten rid of.

John Gifford continued to pursue the matter, and his inquiries continued to uncover more surprises. On April 4, he received a letter from the social worker at the Burrell Home with a page from John's medical record. It revealed a troubling new fact. John's no-code order had been changed the previous September! In the letter, she said: "Enclosed you will find the Doctors Order Sheet for the month of September in 1987. This is the copy of the orders that [the doctor] wrote to rescind the No Code order on John Lovelace." The order sheet itself stated: "Previous order for NO CODE is rescinded. Pt. is a full code. All heroic measures should be attempted in the [case of] cardiac or pulmonary arrest."

John Gifford wrote again to the physician, this time concerning the change in John Lovelace's no-code order. On May 5 he received a response:

> This letter serves to clear up any confusion that may exist over the wishes of John Lovelace, regarding heroic resuscitative measures.
>
> Mr. Lovelace was a patient of mine several years ago, who initially decided that in the event of massive brain hemorrhage or other medical catastrophe, he did not desire heroic resuscitative measures.
>
> Because there was some confusion regarding this documentation on his . . . chart, he was re-approached by me and in the presence of the Burrell Home for Adults Nursing Supervisor . . . he then decided that *he did* want resuscitative measures.
>
> This was duly noted and documented in his chart. Subsequent to this, Mr. Lovelace left the Burrell Home for Adults and my care.
>
> To my knowledge . . . [at] this time, his desire for heroic resuscitative measures remains in force.

The physician who wrote this letter is part of a system that must be questioned. I have not used the physician's name, because to focus on his individual actions, motives, and values would limit what we can learn from the life of John Lovelace and his encounters with our culture. It is the systematic treatment, or mistreatment, of people who are hurt, handicapped, alone, unproductive, or otherwise socially unvalued that I want us to focus on.

I will note, however, that John Gifford was active, concerned, and persistent in uncovering the details of John Lovelace's case. As I wrote to him on May 23, 1988:

> Thanks so much for your recent letter and the copy of [the doctor's letter] to you. I was fascinated by the manner in which he explained his change in John's chart concerning resuscitative measures. It seems incredible that he has not addressed at all the question of John's ability to make an informed decision for a "no code" order. I am more convinced than ever, however, that our actions on this issue have made a real difference in John's best interests. I also believe that other mentally retarded persons may ultimately benefit from our advocacy in John's case.
>
> I also appreciate the copy of your letter to Bob Williams [the owner of the small adult home where John was now living]. I am glad we will have formal documentation that John's current physician has not placed any restrictions on emergency medical treatment in his case.
>
> I visited John at Little Ponderosa [his new home] two weeks ago. I think that the living conditions are a significant improvement for John over what he had at the Burrell Home. The size (17 men), the country atmosphere, and the apparently positive relationships among people there make it appear to be a much more positive environment for him. I talked with Bob Williams for a while and came away feeling that he has a genuine and personal concern for the residents of his facility.
>
> As always, I appreciate the energy and commitment you are giving to the concern we share for John Lovelace and the larger implications of his case. I will be calling soon just to chat about some other information I have found on John's background. Take care.

In early June, John Gifford wrote saying that he was pleased that things seemed to be better for John Lovelace in his new home. More importantly, however, he told me that he was leaving the Department for the Rights of the Disabled that same day. He expressed best wishes for John and said that he was glad to have been able to work for John's well-being. Though I still have never met John Gifford, on John Lovelace's behalf, I thank him.

Chapter 5

Patient 6839: Discharged to Zenia's Love

The medical notes for Patient 6839 at the Virginia Colony for the Feebleminded and Epileptics—Lynchburg State Colony—begin on the day of his admission, October 14, 1948, when his foster mother, Mrs. Hunter, brought him in for admission. Eighteen-year-old John Lovelace, a "simple feebleminded individual," was found to be in fair physical condition. Over the next few days, he was tested for several diseases and X-rayed. No problems were found. He was placed first on Ward 19, then moved to Ward 4, then to Ward 10. The moves seem to have been part of a normal process of finding the most appropriate living area for him.

On November 16, just over a month after his admission to the institution, John went home to Martinsville on a ten-day pass. The notes indicate that seven days later his pass was converted to a parole in the care of his foster mother until January 1, 1949. In December, his parole was extended until February 1. The note for February 1 reads:

> Mother of patient returned him to the Colony today and reported to Dr. Harrell [the superintendent] that John had a job in a sawmill and [was] getting along fine. She asked for an extension of the furlough and this was granted through March 1, 1949.

This furlough was then again extended until March 31, when Mrs. Hunter returned John to the Colony. The notes for that day indicate that she hoped to soon take him back to Martinsville again.

> Letter request for return of parole . . . produced by Mrs. W. I. Hunter, Martinsville, Virginia, custodian of above named patient. Patient pleasant, immature, clean, neat, tidy, in excellent state of health, free from evidence of infectious disease or somatic malady. Patient has been working, $.70 per hour, weather permitting with Messrs. Morris Doyle Lumber Company, total wages $58.40. Camp [the lumber camp] removed to other area. Now hopes to be a "fixer" in local textile mill. Mrs. Hunter reports excellent community adjustment, patient for re-evaluation, and re-check dental, physical, X-ray and psychology; and hopes for recommendation of indoor mill employment under direction. Patient readily and cheerfully goes to Hospital Ward.

Two weeks later, John was again paroled to the care of his foster mother. At this point he had been on the rolls of the institution for seven months but had been in residence only six weeks. Letters Mrs. Hunter wrote to John at the Colony help explain why John was only partially institutionalized. They are printed here as they were written. The grammar and spelling must be understood as expressions from a poor woman with limited education but, as will be seen, a wealth of compassion.

> 1–22 1948
>
> D. L. Harrell Jr. M.D.
>
> Dear sir
>
> in Regards to my son John R. Lovelace that I have at home on a ten day visit he seems very well and so Happy to be at home that I am asking if you will Extend his visit for some time and if he does not get a long all Right I will Braing back there. I will be Responsible for him untill you think it best to braing him back there.
>
> Yours very truly

Mrs. Hunter wrote several other times requesting the parole extensions that John was granted. One letter, written after she had returned him to the Colony for examinations and evaluations, particularly shows her concern for John:

4-12 1949

D. L. Harrell Jr. M.D.

Dear Sir

I did Return John R. Lovelace to the Colony on March 31 not that I found it necessary to do so as his conduct was about perfect while he was here but you wanted him for further treatment of some kind have you completed your study of him and can you give me a sertificate so he can work he has a chance now to learn a trade which is much higher work than he has been doing and much better pay and lots safer it is under union and he can not work there unless I can get sertificate from you stating he is capable of working unless we can Hurry things up a bit I am afraid he will loose this chance at learning a trade so please see what you can do and let me [know] real soon.

Yours very truly

John returned to the Colony briefly in July 1949, when he was sterilized. The medical staff at the institution had recommended this, and Mrs. Hunter agreed that it was a good idea. As discussed earlier, at the time it would have been viewed as serving society's—and John's—best interests.

John was discharged from the state colony in March 1951. He had officially been a patient at the institution for almost two and a half years, though he had actually lived there less than two months. Most of the time he had been in Martinsville with the person who seems to have cared more for him than anyone else did or would: Mrs. Hunter. Prior to John's discharge, a social worker at the Colony had written Mrs. Hunter explaining that it was customary to discharge a patient who had been on parole as long as John, and asking how he had been doing at home. Mrs. Hunter's reply shows she was ready for John's ties to the institution to be severed completely, and hopeful for her adopted son's future.

February 20 1951 Martinsville, Va.

. . . I do not see any reason why my son John R. Lovelace should not be discharge from the Institution as he has not given any trouble in any way since he has been home and has been working with the Lester Hardwood Flooring Co. for the past 9 months and he works with sirule Hundred men and gets on with them all right as far as I know he makes ninty cts a hour and will get a bonus twice a year after working his first 6 months and most of the time he works nine hours a day and is unusual good about going on his job and as far as I can see he is living a very normal Life No drinking no smoking attends church regular and dose not seem to care much for women that is I very seldom even see him with one So I think he can make it all right now and thank you very much for your kindness in writing to me.

Yours very truly

The social worker must have followed up on this letter with a visit or telephone call. In a letter to the Department of Public Welfare in Martinsville about John's upcoming discharge, she described in more detail his positive life in the community.

I talked with Mr. and Mrs. Hunter, Foster Parents, of the above named man. They seemed to be very pleased with John's adjustment. It seems that he has a job with Lester Lumber Company and is doing well in this work. He does not make friends easily, but he and his father are getting along much better and they attend movies and church together. These two activities are the boy's main social outlets. He pays his mother so much a week toward his room and board. Mrs. Hunter stated that it was the boy's desire to do this and she thought that maybe it was a good thing since it gave him the feeling of standing on his feet. He has remained well physically since he has returned; with the exception of an appendix operation, he has had no illnesses. Mrs. Hunter also stated that he was much calmer and was not subject to fits of anger as he was before.

They are real pleased with his being home and hope that they will be able to keep him.

John's foster mother's full name was Zenia Leslie Hunter. I am convinced that she deeply loved her foster son, as her letters reflect a genuine and persevering concern for him. John knew that he had been born

COMMONWEALTH OF VIRGINIA

DEPARTMENT OF MENTAL HYGIENE AND HOSPITALS

CERTIFICATE OF DISCHARGE

LYNCHBURG STATE COLONY
(Name of Hospital or Colony)

Colony, *Virginia*, March 19 1951

THIS IS TO CERTIFY, THAT John Richard Lovelace *Register No.* FM-6839
of Martinsville, *who was committed* May 11 1948
in Martinsville County/*City to*
the Lynchburg State Colony *as** Feebleminded
Name of Hospital or Colony

*is hereby this day discharged as*** Improved and capable of self-support, *and a copy of this certificate is ordered to be filed with the Commitment Papers in the Clerk's Office of the said* County/*City of* Martinsville *Virginia.*

H. N. [illegible]
Acting Superintendent

*Insane, epileptic, feeble-minded or inebriate.
**Restored, improved, unimproved or not insane, epileptic, feeble-minded or inebriate.

Note—Make in duplicate:
One copy for the patient
One copy to the County/City Clerk to be filed with the commitment papers

See Va. Code, Sec. 1028 and 1046

Photocopy of John's Certificate of Discharge, March 19, 1951.

to another woman, but he also knew that Mrs. Hunter was the source of his nurturance.

When I first talked with John about his background, what he said about his mother confused me. His speech is very difficult to understand and I was not sure how much of my confusion was due to my misunderstanding of what he was saying, and how much of it might be due to a problem with John's memory of his childhood. He spoke of his mother as being dead, telling me on one occasion that she was "killed by a boy" but on another that his mother had been hit by a car. Months later my confusion was cleared up after I did some digging into courthouse records and newspaper files in Martinsville.

Etta Lovelace, John's birth mother, was, indeed, "killed by a boy." In 1936, when John was six years old and living with the Hunters, Etta Lovelace was working as a domestic helper in a home outside of Martinsville. One morning as she was churning butter in the kitchen of the house, the fifteen-year-old son of the family passed through the kitchen carrying a rifle on his way to go outside. His rifle accidentally fired and Etta was killed. The *Martinsville Daily Bulletin* described the accident this way:

> Sheriff J. M. Davis and Coroner J. W. Simmons, called to the scene of the shooting for an inquest, learned that young Turner had picked up the gun, a .22 calibre rifle, in a bedroom of the home to go outside and do a little target shooting. As he passed through the kitchen and started out the door, he attempted to unbreech the weapon, and as he did so, it accidentally went off, the discharge striking the woman who was nearby churning, the bullet entering the right side of the abdomen. The woman died within a minute after being wounded. A sister of the youth, Virginia Turner, was washing dishes and barely missed being in the range of the bullet.
>
> Young Turner said he was unaware that the gun was loaded, that he was in the act of unbreeching it when it accidentally went off.

Etta was described in the article as being the daughter of the late John Lovelace, whose obituary, in fact, appeared in the *Daily Bulletin* on April 1, 1932. One of the first bits of information that I shared with John as I attempted to trace his personal history was that he was very likely named for his maternal grandfather. He was pleased with this idea.

Two days after Etta's death, the *Daily Bulletin* reported that the Turner boy had been cleared of any charges in the killing. Technical charges of manslaughter were dropped after the case was heard in the county court. This article also mentioned that Etta had been living with the Turner family since the death of her father.

John was so young when his mother died that his memories of her are naturally vague. He has not been able to tell me whether he saw her often or ever. He simply remembers that she had "long hair and she was pretty." It is likely that Mrs. Hunter instilled in him the memory that Etta was killed by a boy with a gun. Whatever the case, that is all that he has to remember her by. Her death does not seem to be a traumatic recollection for him.

In contrast, the only time I have seen John openly weep was when he tried to tell that his mother had been hit by a car. As I sorted out my confusion over the two stories of the gun and the car, I understood why the latter story moved him so. The woman who was killed by an automobile was John's real mother, his nurturer, protector, and encourager: Mrs. Hunter.

Three years after John was discharged from the Colony at his foster mother's request, she was killed on a highway outside of Martinsville. Apparently, John's life had been going well, with no reports to the contrary. Then he lost the most important person in his life, the one person who really cared about him. The *Bulletin* reported:

> Mrs. Zenia Leslie Hunter, 59-year-old North Martinsville resident, was killed early Tuesday night when struck by an automobile. . . . The accident occurred on route 890 near Snow Creek, in Franklin County, 15 miles north of Martinsville. . . . Mrs. Hunter was believed to have been waiting by the roadside for the Rocky Mount–Martinsville bus when she saw a motor vehicle approaching from the north. In attempting to cross from the eastside to the westside of the highway, she was struck . . . in the center of the southbound lane of the highway. . . . Mrs. Hunter died en route to the Martinsville General Hospital. Death resulted from head and internal injuries. . . . Mrs. Hunter, born in Greyson County in 1895, had made her home here for the past 27 years. She was a member of the Church of Jesus Christ of Latter Day Saints.
>
> Surviving are her husband, William I. Hunter; one daughter . . . ; a foster son, John Lovelace, and three grandchildren.

When Mrs. Hunter died on the highway that evening, much of the hope and potential in John Lovelace's life died with her. His mother, his advocate, the one who most clearly knew him as a human being, was gone.

Chapter 6

In and Out of an Institution

In the early afternoon of September 9, 1957, John Lovelace was re-admitted to the state colony—by then known as the Lynchburg Training School and Hospital. He was given a new patient number, 8998. He had been brought to the institution by the Hunters' daughter, who identified herself on an admissions questionnaire as having no relation to John, though on another form she did indicate that she was a friend. The Hunters' daughter had, in fact, petitioned John's admission, saying that he could not care for himself and that he had no living relatives. Prior to his admission, he had been living in a rooming house in Martinsville.

The physician who examined John upon his admission noted that though syphilis had been mentioned in the past as a possible reason for John's disabilities, John was "completely without the stigmata of congenital syphilis." I had noticed too that according to earlier records, John had tested negative for syphilis, as had Etta Lovelace when she was institutionalized for sterilization. The physician further noted that the "general picture is of natal trauma." He diagnosed John as having cerebral palsy and associated mental retardation—an assessment much more consistent with what I have read and observed about John. I also believe that the "drawing spells" that he was reported to have had as an infant could have been seizures. John has had seizures all of his life, not uncommon with cerebral palsy and mental retardation. His seizures are fairly well controlled now with medication, with none noted for several years.

After testing John, a psychologist found "decided improvement in the test results compared with those of previous commitment." He had apparently learned to make maximum use of his capacity and "could probably continue to assist in his own care as he did in the past but since there is no one to give him any good supervision, he will probably need to remain here." This sad observation proved true. The first time he had been committed, back in 1948, he had spent only weeks actually living at the institution; the rest of the time he was on parole with Mrs. Hunter. This time, John would spend twenty-two years in the Lynchburg Training School and Hospital, with only a few days outside its gates. He was twenty-seven when he was committed; he would be forty-nine before he left. During those twenty-two years, he would completely lose the world he had known before. With all ties of relationship and friendship severed, he would find himself completely alone at the end of those twenty-two years.

Early in John's commitment in the institution, a psychologist noticed that John was sensitive about his speech defect. She said that he apparently tried to conceal the defect by talking in a voice too low to be heard. "When he speaks in a usual tone, he is able to communicate rather well. When asked to repeat, he not only becomes upset and lowers his voice but actually seems to get confused on what he is trying to say. These characteristics, of course, interfere with demonstration of his actual functioning level." As I've already mentioned, communication continues to be a problem for John today. Understanding John is difficult even when you have become accustomed to his speech pattern. He, of course, gets frustrated when he is not understood even after repeated attempts. I often wonder what John could tell about his life if we could only understand him.

The first two years that John was in the institution he went home to Martinsville for Christmas, each time spending at least a week sharing the holiday with Mrs. Hunter's daughter and her family. The third year he did not go home for Christmas. Instead, Mrs. Hunter's daughter sent him a package—she had written to John's social worker earlier asking for his clothing sizes—and a letter.

In November 1961, John's social worker wrote to the Hunters' daughter suggesting a Christmas visit for John.

It has been several years [at that point, three] since John Lovelace has had a vacation away from the institution, and he has asked if it might be possible for you to have him for a short visit during the Christmas holidays this year. It would mean a great deal to John to be able to be in a home for a few days, and we would appreciate very much your taking him. If it is not convenient for you to have him over Christmas Day, perhaps we can arrange a New Year's visit. John has money and could pay his own transportation by bus.

We are enclosing a vacation form and a list of furlough instructions to help you in planning a trip for John, and we look forward to hearing from you.

As a result of the letter, John went home on a bus and stayed a week. The next year, a similar letter was sent, this one signed by the superintendent. This time the response was different.

Dear Mr. Nagler,

It is impossible at this time for me to have John home. The way that I am working there would be no one home all day and John would be by himself. I think Christmas would mean more to him there with the nice Christmas program you have set up.

Maybe we can have him home during the spring vacation. I will be on vacation and be at home with him.

I am very sorry that I have to say no at this time.

Letters continued to go out for several years around the holidays. But there never was another response. A final attempt to contact the family was made in January 1978.

We are writing to bring you up to date on Mr. Lovelace's progress. He was recently transferred from living unit 2D to 3D within the Social Skills Center. He was promoted as a result of his continued good behavior. We feel that he is making progress. He seems to understand why he must learn to deal with anger in a more constructive manner than acting out at others. We hope he will continue

> to work with us. Family contact can be used to encourage appropriate behavior. We urge you and other interested individuals to visit and correspond frequently. You are invited to meet with us to discuss the programs Mr. Lovelace is enrolled in. We hope to hear from you soon.

The letter was returned marked "Addressee Unknown." John's last tie to family and community had been severed.

My description of the breaking of bonds between this family and John is not meant to be condemnatory. Rather, I offer it as an example of a systematic tendency. Institutions for people who are mentally retarded, like other residential institutions, function to isolate their residents, even from their own families. The term *colony* was very appropriate. These institutions *were* colonies, of people exiled from the "homeland" of their culture, people who tended to be forgotten by their culture. The longer they remained colonized, the more likely that their ties to family and community would weaken. If they stayed long enough, the chances were great that those ties would unravel completely. Most mental retardation institutions have their own graveyards for good reasons. People who live in institutions for most of their lives are at high risk of outliving their connections to the external world. When they die, there is no one to claim them, no one from the outside world to grieve for them. They do not escape the colony even in death. Some families do maintain interest and contact, and continue to care. But maintaining ties across institutional walls is very hard work. It takes a strong family or friend or community to resist separation's wearing away of bonds. It is no accident that most of the large mental retardation institutions were built in out-of-the-way places. They were intended to be not a part of society but apart from society. This was as true of the occupants as of the buildings.

The last letter referred to John's need to learn to control his anger. This has been, and continues to be, a long-standing problem for him. It was John's anger that first prompted Mrs. Hunter to have him institutionalized. The shock of that separation from her may have been one of the reasons for his apparent dramatic and positive change, and quick parole and discharge. I suspect that after her death, angry outbursts may have led to his second commitment. I think that I can

Photocopies of pictures taken of John Lovelace during his years at Lynchburg Training School and Hospital.

understand his anger. I imagine that if I had grown up with the physical, social, and psychological wounds that he had, I might be even angrier. I have seen John, when frustrated, frightened, or hurting, react with anger, not knowing what else to do. Anger is a basic and strong emotion, one readily available to us. John has used it, I am convinced, as a means of trying to survive. Unfortunately, his angry outbursts have also caused him much suffering.

During his long stay in the Lynchburg Training School and Hospital from 1957 to 1979, John was involved in more than thirty serious fights. This number may be just the tip of the iceberg—fights serious enough to be written up in his record. Loosened teeth, abrasions, lacerations, and stitches were commonplace in his life. Though he often took the first swing, he appears to have usually been on the losing side of his battles. His poor balance and lack of coordination did not serve him well in these altercations. He was also punished for these fights. For example, for June 3, 1960, his record shows: "John got into a fight with Harvey B. Discipline: Lock up on ward 22C, for three days."

John's records have consistently shown that he likes to work. My own experience with him verifies this. He likes to be busy and useful. He likes to earn money. Having a little pocket money seems to be one of the few symbols available to him of some independence in his life. And work is often an earned privilege in all kinds of institutions: For inmates, patients, and others, to be trusted to work is to have elevated status.

A beloved former professor of mine, Ignacy Goldberg, now retired from Columbia University's Teachers College, once talked with me about his experience as an administrator in an institution in the Midwest. He saw institutions for mentally retarded people as containing three cultures. The first consisted of the "retarded retarded" (today we would probably call them severely retarded), who really needed care. Then there were the "normal retarded," people who would be considered retarded outside the institution but who, within the institution, were normal, everyday citizens; these moderately retarded individuals were the ones who cared for the "retarded retarded." Finally, there was the group Dr. Goldberg called the "minimally gifted"—mildly retarded people and individuals wrongly classified as retarded. Their role in the institution was to set the actual day-to-day policy, create the atmosphere of the place, and interact socially with the staff.

In some cases, the work done by patients was not officially sanctioned or recognized. The more able patients, as described above, did work that was assigned to the paid staff, in return for cigarettes, privileges, praise, and tips. In other cases, formal work programs provided the patients rewards or minimal payment for their efforts. In 1959, John was described in his patient notes as "working patient, helps to take care of patients." This was obviously an officially recognized program. (His work and angry outbursts were sometimes incompatible. A note from 1965 said, "During the daytime he does good work, according to the attendant, but occasionally has to be reprimanded because he has a rather explosive temper.") Several times during the decade of the sixties, the notes referred to him as a "working boy." (The use of the term *boy* for a man in his late thirties recalls its offensive use as a term for black men.) It was common in institutions for "working patients" to do much of the dressing, bathing, and toileting of the less able patients, as reflected in a 1968 entry in John's medical file: "Patient slipped when coming out of the doorway of the tub room with [another] patient in his arms. FINDINGS: Contusion of the right hip."

During the early seventies, work programs that were intended to provide training and develop skills that could eventually be used outside the institution became common. This was part of the growing movement toward the deinstitutionalization of patients who could be prepared to live in the community. John was involved in what was called the Work Activity Center. There again, a tension existed between his ability to work well and his behavior problems. The notes for March 1973 said, "The Work Activity Center has reported that Mr. Lovelace has been suspended from this placement several times because of his abusive behavior. . . . It is reported, however, that Mr. Lovelace is a good worker and has been given added responsibilities because of this." John eventually proved himself in this program and was employed by a sheltered workshop in Lynchburg. Before his release, he also worked days at Jefferson Car Wash in Lynchburg and did yardwork for a local physician.

The deinstitutionalization movement reached its peak in the latter half of the seventies. Those in professional and political circles had come to embrace the idea that people with disabilities should be placed in communities rather than in institutions, and people were moved out of institutions in large numbers. John Lovelace was one of them.

On May 29, 1979, John was placed on leave at Kennedy House, an adult home in Martinsville. He also went to work at a sheltered workshop there. Plans were made to place him in a job elsewhere in Martinsville after he completed training at the workshop. After a few months, he was described as having adjusted well to his new job and home. Professionals at the Lynchburg Training School and Hospital and at Kennedy House agreed that the time had come for John to be discharged from the institution.

DMH 2

COMMONWEALTH OF VIRGINIA

Department of Mental Health and Mental Retardation

CERTIFICATE OF DISCHARGE
Section 37.1-98 Code of Virginia
Lynchburg Training School and Hospital
Facility

Lynchburg, Virginia November 21, 1979

This is to Certify that John Richard Lovelace, Reg. No. 8998

of Martinsville who was admitted September 9, 1957

by Voluntary Admission from
(Voluntary Admission, or Involuntary Admission)

Martinsville ~~County~~/City to LTSH
(Name of Facility)

as* Mentally Deficient is hereby discharged as** Not recovered but his discharge, in the opinion of the Director, will not be detrimental to the public welfare or injurious to himself.

Signed Kay Nelson, MD
Director

* Mentally Ill, Mentally Deficient, Inebriate, Drug Addict

** Recovered, Not Mentally Ill, Not Recovered but his/her discharge, in the opinion of the Director, will not be detrimental to the public welfare or injurious to himself/herself.

Make in Duplicate one copy to Department
one copy record

Photocopy of John's Certificate of Discharge, November 21, 1979.

On November 20, 1979, John received a letter from his social worker that was also signed by the director of the Lynchburg Training School and Hospital and two other professionals who had helped design and implement John's deinstitutionalization program.

Dear John:

I am writing to let you know that your discharge is final on November 21, 1979.

If you remember from my last visit with you, this will mean that you are now completely free from Lynchburg Training School and Hospital. You can live and work in Martinsville, forever, just like all other men in our country.

Please remember to try and save your money, and to listen to what Ms. Robertson, the nurses, the aides, and Mr. Poole tell you. They care a lot about you and want to help you do what is best. Also, you must remember to control your temper and not get in any fights.

All of us here at the Lynchburg Training School and Hospital are very, very proud of how well you are doing in Martinsville. We are very happy to be able to give you your discharge. I have enjoyed working with you, and will come to visit you again when I am in Martinsville.

Chapter 7

Deinstitutionalization

"You are now completely free from Lynchburg Training School and Hospital," said the letter confirming John's discharge. "You can live and work in Martinsville, forever, just like all other men in our country." These encouraging and hopeful words, written by John's social worker at Lynchburg, would not prove prophetic. John was discharged in November 1979. He was back at the Training School in four months.

On March 28, 1980, John was admitted to the Social Skills Center at Lynchburg Training School and Hospital on an emergency basis. His admission was classified as respite care, and his stay was limited to 21 days. The Social Skills Center at the Training School specialized in working with mentally retarded people to control serious behavior problems. John's behavior was becoming more and more problematic. Despite his social worker's optimism when John was discharged, things had apparently not gone well at the Kennedy House, the adult home to which he'd been discharged. In fact, before being returned to the Training School, John had been committed to Central State Hospital, because he had gotten into a fight with another resident at Kennedy and knocked out two of the other man's teeth.

Central State Hospital is a large psychiatric facility. John was admitted there on the assumption that his violent behavior might have been the result of a psychotic episode. Examiners there soon diagnosed him as having "no psychosis" and ordered him discharged.

Unfortunately, there was no place to send him. Finally, an official in the Office of the Commissioner of Mental Retardation made a special request to the Training Center that John be admitted on a respite basis.

John's behavior while at the Training Center was exemplary. His release summary when he was discharged on April 18 was positive: "If respite was for an extended period of time, placement on a unit less restrictive than the Social Skills Center [would be recommended]. . . . John was noted to interact well with peers and to be cooperative with staff members. He participated in unit activities and classes."

John was discharged from the Training Center to another psychiatric facility. After a short stay there, he was placed in a large adult home in Roanoke. Two years later, he was moved to another adult home in the same city, where he lived for two and a half years. After spending about a month in the Roanoke Valley Psychiatric Center, he was then placed in the Burrell Home for Adults, where he was living when I met him. In the six years since he had been "deinstitutionalized," John had been placed in nine different settings. The movement toward community-based placement for people who are mentally retarded had promised a community that did not seem to exist for John.

John's anger seemed to grow worse with each change of placement. In fact, probably because of his angry outbursts, his diagnosis during this time was changed from mental retardation to mental illness. His many transfers have made tracing his records to learn more about his life during that period almost impossible, but clearly, he was growing more and more desperate and disoriented, and was coming to be perceived as more and more of a problem. And despite being deinstitutionalized six years earlier, by the time I came to know him, John had become "reinstitutionalized" in the adult home system, where there was no campaign to move people out. Ironically, this institutional system was itself a product of the deinstitutionalization movement. The small, and not so small, private institutions, operated for profit, that make up this system became the receptacles for many, if not most, of the individuals who were moved out of institutions for the mentally ill and mentally retarded. These "homes" are the so-called community placements for many of those who were supposed to be leaving the restrictive environments of the institutions.

When I first visited John in 1987, I was immediately taken with the institutional feel of the adult home where he was living. It had the look and smell of institutions I had visited years before. In recent years, "real" institutions have been diligently changed to make them look less institutional. There are more bright colors on walls. Windows have curtains or drapes. Pictures, decorations, and variety have supplanted clinical standardization and walls of "institutional green."

The Burrell Home for Adults, however, seemed unabashedly institutional and unconcerned about appearances. Its sameness, drabness, and worn edges reminded me of what I had read of and seen in large state institutions before they were opened up to public scrutiny and criticism. In fact, this was my first visit to a large, privately operated adult home. I had been in several small, publicly funded adult homes, and had found them to be positive environments for their residents. This was something different. I was appalled!

I had tried to visualize the Burrell Home for Adults as I'd driven the fifty miles from Lynchburg to Roanoke. I knew nothing in advance of the home's size, history, or organization. When I pulled into the parking lot, I was amazed. I knew of the building by another name, having passed near it many times years before, though I had never actually seen it before.

I was born in Roanoke and lived there until I left for college. During the years of my childhood, blacks were forbidden admission to and treatment in "white" hospitals. They could clean these hospitals, including the one where I was born, but they couldn't receive medical care there. I remember, as a child, while passing through the "colored section" of town on our way to visit relatives, hearing comments about Burrell Memorial, the "colored hospital" that was "just over that hill." This was the building I was about to enter to visit John.

The term *home* connotes for me a personal place, a place that belongs to its inhabitants and a place where individuality is paramount. A home is where you can be "yourself" and where the inhabitants know one another well, even if they don't live in complete harmony. I find particularly disturbing the use of the word *home* for impersonal, anonymous places where people have little control over their own lives. (One summer while I was in college, I worked at a place whose name was formed into the stone arch over the front door: the Virginia Home for Incurables. It was an old facility even then, though it had undergone some positive changes in philosophy and operation. Still, I often wondered how the residents there felt about passing through a doorway that so proscribed their destinies.)

The home that I visited that Sunday afternoon was not much like a home. As I came up the walkway, there were many people sitting and standing on the lawn and around the entrance. As I have found in other similar settings, the people there seemed almost startled at being spoken to. They seemed to expect not to be seen, having learned that they are socially invisible. I was reminded of Ralph Ellison's assertion in *The Invisible Man* that the real problem of being black in America lies in not being seen as an individual human being.

Fortunately, I had gotten directions from John's social worker as to how to find John once I was at the Burrell Home, because when I walked into the lobby of the building I found no receptionist. Indeed, I appeared to be the only visitor at the time. I went to the third floor, as the social worker had told me, and found John's room, but he was not there. When I inquired at the nurse's station, I was told to look in the smoking lounge at the end of the hall. There he was with several other people in a small room thick with smoke. John was smoking and looking at the floor. The others took little note as I entered the room and it was a while before John looked up. When he did look up, I called him by name, and reminded him of my name. This was the first time that I had seen him since the camping weekend, and so I told him that we had met there. He immediately perked up: Camp Virginia Jaycee is a happy memory for many who go there. John seemed glad to have a visitor and was more than willing to show me around.

As we walked through each floor of the old hospital building, I came to a sad realization: Though it was Sunday afternoon, the prime time for visitors in a place like this, I was the only visitor. The reality of that sharpened as we encountered other residents of the home. They wanted to talk, to show me things, pictures. John wanted to keep moving, as if having a visitor was too precious an event to share.

Months later, an employee of the Burrell Home confided "off the record" that Burrell was the "end of the line" for old and disabled people who were, for the most part, poor and alone. Its residents simply had nowhere else to be. That certainly matches my impression of that Sunday afternoon when I first visited John.

We ended our tour in John's room. The only decorations I saw were the crafts he had made during our camping weekend. We sat on his bed and talked. I explained that I wanted to know more about his health, and about what should be done if he got very sick. I talked a bit about the no-code order, but I don't think that he fully comprehended what I was talking about. I then asked if he would be willing to sign a form so that a lawyer and I could look at his records. He readily agreed. I am sure that his willingness had more to do with his identification of me with the camping weekend than with any real understanding of what I was trying to do. While we were on tour, he had introduced me to several people as the "man from camp."

John executed his signature slowly and with care, as I have seen him do many times since. His vision was poor even then, and he had to put his face close to the paper as he wrote. After completing his name, he sat back with a look of satisfaction.

I stayed awhile longer and then headed back for Lynchburg. As I drove home, I reflected on what I had seen that afternoon. For more than a decade, I had been lecturing to students on the progress of the deinstitutionalization movement and the promise it held for better lives for mentally retarded people. Yet, the "community-based" adult home that I had just left, with its more than 200 residents, looked more like an institution than the state institutions I had visited in recent years. I arrived home saddened and perplexed.

It would be easy to condemn the existence of a place like the Burrell Home for Adults, and decry its way of operating. It would be easy, and perhaps satisfying in a way, to blame the problems of people like John on particular people, programs, and facilities. To do so is tempting but it is incorrect. The problem is, as I said in an earlier chapter, systemic. What we really encounter when we examine the life of a person like John Lovelace is a failure in our will as a culture to do anything better with people "at the bottom": those who are poor, old, disabled, and unproductive; people who are problems.

In 1989 I met a talented young journalist with the *Roanoke Times and World News.* Mike Hudson was just completing a six-month study of the adult home system in Virginia. His findings, published as a series by the newspaper, captured the attention of the public and of professionals and lawmakers within the state and beyond.

Mike traced the beginnings of Virginia's adult homes to what had been commonly known as "old-folks homes"—places where elderly people who did not require nursing care could go to live out their final years in a quiet and safe environment. These were mostly small, mom-and-pop operations averaging about twenty-four residents each.

The nature of these businesses changed dramatically in the 1970s when the state institutions released many of their inmates. As people left these facilities, resources to support them in the community were scarce. Not enough publicly supported group homes and other appropriate living arrangements were created to meet the needs of those leaving the institutions. This void fostered the development of the private adult home industry. Soon these homes had tripled in number, and they were growing in size as well. By 1989, their capacities ranged from 4 to 600 residents, with an average capacity of 47. The residents of these "board and care" facilities include the elderly, mentally retarded people, and people classified as mentally ill. A common denominator for many, however, is poverty.

Though the homes are run for profit, many derive most of their income from public sources. Currently, for each resident dependent on federal Supplemental Security Income and a state auxiliary grant, an adult home receives about $616 a month. That translates into about $20.50 per day per resident for food, housing, staff, laundry, programs, and profit. Obviously, if the home is to make an attractive profit, the cost per resident must be kept to a minimum. Can we wonder that there are problems in the quality of life and care in these homes?

The state has very low standards for the licensing of adult homes. Staffing requirements are low. Most homes that house primarily people on public assistance pay their workers minimum wage and offer no real training to those hired. As a result, untrained and inexperienced workers are often responsible for caring for some of the most mentally disabled people in the system. There are approximately 20,000 people living in more than 450 adult homes in Virginia. Inspections by state officials are infrequent. Homes found to be in violation of the very low standards that they must meet are rarely penalized. The only penalty on the books is revocation of license, and that is rarely done. After all, if a home's license were revoked, where would its residents go?

Mike Hudson also published some of his findings in an article printed in the magazine *Southern Exposure* in the fall of 1989. His words paint a dismaying portrait of what has happened in some adult homes.

> At Pine Ridge Home for Adults near Farmville, the new owner tangled with a mentally ill resident who refused to leave the kitchen. After the resident kicked him in the stomach, the owner pulled a gun and shot him.
>
> At Arnold's Rest Home near Abingdon, a woman diagnosed with schizophrenia suffered mysteriously broken legs, arms, and ribs. For several days, the only way she could get from her bedroom to the dining room was by dragging herself across the floor on her bottom.
>
> At Hairston's Home for Adults in Martinsville, the owners admitted a 26-year-old mentally ill man convicted of assaulting a resident at another adult home. A few weeks later, he was charged with murdering a 59-year-old resident by pushing him under scalding water.
>
> At Cardinal Home for Adults in Botetourt County, a mentally ill resident threatened to commit suicide. The owner opened up a medicine cabinet, showed him an unloaded gun, and said: "Go ahead."
>
> Thousands of mentally ill [and mentally retarded] people are in danger of abuse and neglect in adult "board and care" homes across Virginia.
>
> They are victims of a handful of untrained or greedy adult home owners who try to squeeze maximum profits out of their businesses. They are victims of a weak-kneed welfare system that has largely failed to police these operations. And they are victims of a tight-fisted state government that has failed to come up with money to improve conditions in poorly run adult homes or find the mentally ill [and retarded] better places to live.

By 1989, conditions in adult homes had also become a national issue. The Government Accounting Office had investigated adult homes in six states, including Virginia, and issued a report that described the horrible conditions found in some of those homes. One home's administrator had instructed his staff to feed a resident only bread and water and to discontinue his medication. The rationale was that the resident was bedridden and "dying anyway." In another home, the owner had sexually abused three female residents, including one who was retarded. She became pregnant and had an abortion.

Also in 1989, the congressional Subcommittee on Health and Long-Term Care issued a report called "Board and Care Homes in America: A National Tragedy." The report estimated that one million Americans live in 68,000 licensed and unlicensed homes. Representative Claude Pepper of Florida, the chairman of the subcommittee, described the care provided in many of these homes as "a tragedy of epic proportions, and a disgraceful failure of public policy." The report emphasized that "regulations for licensed board and care homes are general and some are unenforceable." The following examples were among those highlighted in the subcommittee's report:

> In New Mexico, 10 Alzheimer's patients were found bound to their wheelchairs in spite of a law requiring residents to be able to leave the home under emergency situations of their own power. In California, we investigated the murder of seven residents by an ex-felon manager [of the adult home] who then cashed their Social Security checks. In Maryland, an owner continued to house 11 residents in her burned out home—one resident was robbed of all his possessions. In the District of Columbia, a bedbound elderly woman was found by Subcommittee staff lying in her own urine, begging for food in her roach-infested three-story walk-up room. . . . In Alabama, a home cited for numerous violations by the Subcommittee burned down, injuring two of the home's frail elderly residents several days after the visit. In Virginia, we found 11 former mental patients, two of whom required skilled nursing care, warehoused in an old row house.

Has anything happened as a result of that 1989 report and the other information made public that year about conditions in adult homes across the country? Has anything happened in Virginia as a result of Mike Hudson's investigation of adult homes? The answer to both questions is that little has changed.

Chapter 8

Smoking, Headaches, and Fights

John was admitted to the Burrell Home for Adults on October 15, 1985. As I explained earlier, this was his ninth "home" in six years. The records indicate that he seemed to be doing well during his first few days at Burrell. He was described as adjusting quickly. His records also mention that he was enthusiastic about going back to work at the sheltered workshop where he had worked earlier while living in another adult home. The assessment of his first nine days at Burrell was that he caused "no management problems." The nurse in charge of this first progress report noted, "John appears to be doing well. [He] states he likes Burrell and staff. He states he is ready to return to TMW [the sheltered workshop]. . . . Appointment with. . . counselor Oct. 28 [at] 10:00, "Anger Management" group to start November 5, 9-10:00."

Things appeared to be going well for John. His adjustment to the placement sounded good. His anticipation of returning to work seemed a positive sign. The fact that he had been registered in a program to help him manage his anger looked promising.

The anger management group was a service that had been arranged through the public agency responsible for providing mental health services in the community. A similar agency was responsible for meeting the needs of mentally retarded people in the community. Both agencies were directed by a regional community services board. By the time that John was moved to Burrell, he was no longer receiving any assistance from Mental Retardation Services.

By the summer of 1985, a few months before his admission to Burrell, the focus of his case had become his anger. The question of how this anger related to his mental retardation was not being addressed. His records at Mental Health Services reflect primarily his need for anticonvulsive medication, his aggressive and violent behavior, and his diagnosis as a schizophrenic, as shown in excerpts from the medical notes of a consulting psychiatrist who was seeing him under the auspices of Mental Health:

> 7/10/85 Seen with therapist. . . violent episodes in the last week are reported, including punching others in the face with little provocation. Hospitalization is recommended on a Mental Health Warrant.
>
> 8/14/85 Since last visit, John had an uneventful admission to Roanoke Rehab under my care where he show[ed] no active problems in that setting. He was discharged after a brief weekend stay essentially. Today there are still reports of some irritable behavior on his part that may be provoked by other residents. I am shifting his Mellaril medication so that he gets more during the daytime when these occur. He will now be taking 100 mg., 4 times a day. His Dilantin and Phenobarb are renewed unchanged. . . .
>
> 9/11/85 Seen today for a one week follow-up emergency appointment. Last week, he was started on Amitriptyline to see if an antidepressant could reduce his irritability. As is sometimes seen in schizophrenia, the anti-depressant had the opposite effect and increased his irritability. I am therefore stopping it and going to a more sedative regimen of Thorazine 600 mg. per day. . . .
>
> 2/12/86 . . . John is doing well at the Burrell Home. There are no complaints. His medicine has not been changed since his hospitalization. It is renewed unchanged. . . . He is friendly and in good spirits.

Things were not actually going as smoothly as appeared. John began to experience difficulties early on during his stay at Burrell. His problems did not become critical, however, until May 1986. The daily notes made by the nurses in charge of each shift reveal much about both John's behavior at that time and the staff's perceptions of his behavior. The notes for the afternoon of May 26 show that John was seriously hurt during that shift.

> 5/10/86, 2:10 pm Called to floor from lunch by resident. Arrived to find John lying on floor and bleeding from back of head. Ambulance had been called. . . . Responsive to name but was slightly dazed. 2:25 pm—Ambulance arrived—head bandaged—cervical collar applied—back board used. 2:25 pm—Transported to Roanoke Memorial Hospital. . . .
>
> 5/10/86 Resident was involved in a fight with [another] resident earlier today and sent to emergency room. He returned . . . very calm and quiet. Stitches were needed and given at emergency room. . . . Resident is at present time sitting in smoking room creating no problems, will observe. 8:00—Resident still sitting in smoking room, alert and aware of surroundings. 10:00—Asleep in room. Aroused easily, aware of name, place and date.

I have no evidence of what caused the fight that led to John's injury, or even of whom the fight was with. Knowing John as I have come to, however, I feel confident that the fight concerned cigarettes: Either John was out of cigarettes and was trying to get one, or he feared losing a cigarette.

John is heavily addicted to tobacco. This is not at all unusual for people who have been institutionalized. Cigarettes have traditionally been the one officially sanctioned "vice" among residents of institutions. Those who operate mental health and mental retardation facilities have never acknowledged their residents' normal sex drives and, therefore, have never provided for their healthy expression. Drinking is never allowed. Smoking, however, has been not only allowed but encouraged, used as a means of behavior control. Residents who do what they are told are rewarded with cigarettes, more frequent opportunities to smoke them, or both. Authority figures have parceled out cigarettes one at a time for compliant behavior. And despite the current emphasis on smoke-free environments, the smoking areas of adult homes, institutions, and other places where mentally disabled adults live and work are still cloudy with smoke. Cigarettes, and, to a lesser extent, coffee, are the currency of adult homes and similar places. People *live* for them, having nothing else to look forward to. The cigarette trade controls favors and friendship. Monthly allowances are reckoned in terms of the number of cigarettes they can buy, and visitors are viewed as sources of extra cigarette money. Although there are obviously exceptions, cigarettes and coffee dominate the moment-to-moment consciousness of most residents of adult homes. More addicted than most people in these settings, John becomes very anxious when he thinks of running out. As an ex-smoker, I understand this well. Unfortunately, John cannot be as assured of getting that next pack as I was, or as most smokers are. Facing nicotine cravings that he cannot satisfy, he falls apart and strikes out.

A sampling from the daily nursing notes at Burrell indicates how problematic John's smoking addiction was:

> 6/8/86—June Summary
> Resident sleeps majority of night on 11-7 [the shift]. However, on occasion does stay in smoking lounge all night. Will get upset if he is out of cigarettes and throws chairs and uses abusive language. . . .
>
> 6/9/86, 10:00 pm John was sitting in dayroom and Sherman . . . came up and asked John to give him a cigarette. John said no and Sherman got mad and hit John in the face and head. Then they began to hit each other. Sherman knocked John to the floor and began to kick John on the leg. John kicked him back. . . .
>
> 2/23/87 At 2:45 am, resident Lovelace came to desk demanding cigarettes. After resident was informed that he did not have any smoking materials, he cursed, slammed chairs, kicked doors and

> pounded the plexiglass of the nurse's station with his fists. Resident was asked to return to quarters. Lovelace replied, ". . . not until I get a cigarette." Incident reported to LPN on duty. Resident quiet while nurse on floor. Immediately after departure of duty nurse, resident began cursing and picked up several chairs in the smoking lounge. Lovelace demanded personal smoking materials belonging to staff, but was denied due to his behaviors. Resident responded by charging up to nurse's station with a chair as if to break down the plexiglass around the desk. The nurse on duty was notified again.

Though my explanation may seem simplistic, I am convinced that John's angry outbursts, and the injuries and difficulties that have resulted, have for years been precipitated by his cigarette addiction—and by headaches.

John's earliest records note recurring complaints of headaches. These complaints have often preceded his episodes of disruptive behavior. John has been unable to explain to me how his headaches feel and how long they last, but I wonder if he has been experiencing migraine headaches, or something like them, all of his life. The idea that he may have been suffering great pain, unable to comprehend it himself or to articulate it to others, disturbs me greatly. I raised this possibility at a recent physical examination of John, but nothing was found or reported. An excerpt from John's records at Burrell evinces his headache problems:

> 9/20/86—Sept. Summary
> Resident has been having problems with headaches of late, CAT scan among other testings done, is also encouraged to wear glasses which helps with redness of eyes . . . stays in around Home now that he is having difficulty with headaches. . . . Resident has frequent outbursts of anger. Can become violent at times. Likes to smoke and drink coffee. . . . No plans to discharge at this time.

John was becoming more and more of a problem. In addition to his angry outbursts, other difficulties were beginning to be noticed. In

October 1986, a nurse noted that his gait was becoming worse. He has always walked with a limp and shuffle because of his cerebral palsy, but he was now leaning forward much more markedly. He was also beginning to stumble more frequently as he moved about. In February 1987, he was described as "becoming increasingly worse, John sits down when he is to stand, is starting to wet his clothing. Gait is not as stable as in past months." The change in his gait and coordination may have been related to eye problems he was having that were not recognized as serious at the time but that were treated several months later. Whatever the case, the nurse's notes portray John as a weaker, more disabled person.

On March 17, a licensed practical nurse reported on John's condition and apparently initiated the request for a no-code order for him. In a request to the consulting physician, she wrote, "Resident is sleeping most of the days and complains of severe headaches. . . . When he is not at work [at the sheltered workshop] he is in bed most of day. Appears more lethargic—request follow-up of CAT scan . . . also written excuse for work and an order for 'No Code.'" After examining John, the physician wrote on the bottom of the form, "Please advise of patient's next of kin."

The summary entry in his records for March says, "Resident has appeared to regress—resting more with frequent headaches—has not been going to workshop regularly—Remains continent of bowels and bladder—Appetite good—Less frequent episodes of outbursts noted—Has ordered a 'No Code' status due to condition at this time."

John was treated for his eye ailment in late April. He must have felt better physically after this treatment. His angry outbursts, however, came back with a vengeance. On April 22, he exploded in, as always, the smoking lounge. No reason was noted for his outburst, but I am certain it was the same: a perceived or real inequity in cigarette dealings. John threw chairs and ashtrays, pushed another resident against the wall, defied the staff.

Over the next four months, these episodes continued to occur, always in the smoking lounge. On one occasion, John was handcuffed and taken to an emergency psychiatric center. He stayed there for two weeks and was returned to Burrell.

The final bell rang for John at the Burrell Home for Adults on September 23, 1987. The circumstances are no surprise: "Resident was in dayroom smoking—an argument [arose] between him and Wendell. . . . When we entered the dayroom . . . he struck another resident." The same day, "Helen . . . states that John hit her in the eye for coffee." And then comes the entry that signaled the end of his stay at Burrell: "John was told today he is getting 2 weeks notice to move, Mental Health Services–Mental Retardation notified."

Chapter 9

Institutionalization, Sterilization, and Deinstitutionalization

On November 3, 1948, John's foster mother wrote to the superintendent of the Lynchburg Training School and Hospital. John had been admitted only a month before, but his mother's letter clearly shows that she was anxious to have him back home with her. Mrs. Hunter would repeatedly request that John be allowed to come home on "furlough" or "parole." As a result, and as was pointed out earlier, John actually spent very little time in the institution during his first commitment there. Mrs. Hunter's November letter also reveals a concern she had regarding John and one reason, probably the primary reason, that she wanted him to be committed in the first place. Again, I have not edited the language of her letters but have left them to reflect the character of this woman with little education but a great depth of compassion for her foster son.

> In regard to my son John R. Lovelace a patient there I was down to see him 31 of October and found him very Home sick and seems to be unable to adjust him self in any way and [I] have allways new his General Health means a better mind. Now would you be so kind as to Paroll this Boy to me as soon as he has had the necessary medical treatment such as being Stirrel and having his Tonisal and Adinois removed. I kindly would like for you to do that much while he is there. I am unable to have that done here. Reason—mostly lack of funds to pay off with but you can do this for us and Paroll

him in our care I will try to get his General health up again and he might go on sevrile years with[out] giving any trouble Will I need any one signature other than myself and Husband I don't want to come down there unprepared to sign papers.

Yours truly, Mr.& Mrs. W I Hunter

Clearly, Mrs. Hunter felt that sterilization was an important health measure for John. It is interesting that she grouped it with removal of his tonsils and adenoids as a preventative procedure that would be good for him, and that she could not otherwise afford to provide for him. Her attitude in this regard reflects the conventional wisdom of the time: that the greatest threat that people considered retarded or otherwise incompetent posed to society, and to themselves, was that of the reproduction of bad traits, particularly in children for whom they were patently unable to care properly.

Mrs. Hunter probably viewed sterilization as something that she, as a good mother, had a responsibility to seek for her son—a safeguard he needed that she couldn't afford. By appealing to the Training School for it, she was doing the best she could for her child. Of course, the same conventional wisdom prevailed at the Lynchburg Training School and Hospital. A staff meeting of physicians, psychologists, and social workers was convened on April 4, 1949. Their report ended with the comment: "Eugenic sterilization is emphatically recommended." In accordance with Mrs. Hunter's request and the staff recommendation, on July 18, 1949, John was sterilized.

Proponents of eugenics, sometimes called the "science of race improvement," claimed that the idea was based on scientific principles. It gained widespread acceptance in medicine, genetics, and the social sciences during the early part of this century and heavily influenced both politicians and practitioners in all of the human services fields. As a result, several generations of the poor, the disabled, and the otherwise socially disadvantaged felt the impact of this philosophy and the practices it spawned. Basically, eugenics advocated the reproductive control of people deemed to have poor genetic makeups. (Certain people were thought to carry "bad seeds"—the sources of mental retardation, mental illness, epilepsy, alcoholism, criminality, and even poverty.) Eugenics enthusiasts also felt that people of "good stock" should be encouraged to have large families, thereby passing on their genetic superiority to increasing numbers of offspring.

The primary means for controlling the reproduction of the "genetically inferior" was sterilization. The state of Virginia passed a sterilization law in 1924 that was declared constitutional by the U.S. Supreme Court in 1927, in the test case of *Buck* v. *Bell*. The Court's decision in this case effectively gave state governments the right to sterilize, even against their will and the wishes of their families, persons found to be incompetent by standards set by the state.

In the pivotal case, Carrie Buck was a seventeen-year-old who had an illegitimate child and on this basis was found to be morally and mentally defective. She was institutionalized at the Lynchburg Colony (later the Training School and Hospital), which was superintended at the time of the test case by Dr. John Bell. Her mother, a prostitute, had been institutionalized there a few years earlier on similar charges. The claim was made that Carrie's illegitimate child was also "feebleminded" and thus represented the third generation of genetic defectiveness. This claim was the basis of the argument that Carrie should be sterilized to prevent any further transmission of her mental and social defects. Carrie's sterilization following the Supreme Court decision became the precedent for more than 50,000 such procedures in the United States. The practice continued in many states for decades, with some states performing involuntary sterilizations into the 1970s. Ironically, Carrie's illegitimate child, Vivian, was an honor student in her elementary school. The "third generation of imbecile" claim that had helped form the Supreme Court's decision proved to be invalid. In fact, research for a book that I wrote with K. Ray Nelson, entitled *The Sterilization of Carrie Buck*, provided evidence that Carrie herself was not mentally retarded. She was simply an impoverished girl with few opportunities and fewer advocates. It was her circumstances that made her the choice of eugenicists who wished to convince others of the need to control the reproductive capacities of specific populations.

Several years ago, my friend Eric Juengst—then a professor of ethics at Penn State's College of Medicine and now head of the Ethics Division of the Human Genome Project—happened on a used book sale, where he found a copy of a genetics text published in 1926. He bought the book, primarily because its table of contents showed the connections that were being made at the time among genetics, eugenics, race and social problems, and population control. That was interesting enough, but after buying the book, he found that it was inscribed as belonging to a University of Pittsburgh medical student in the late twenties. Even more interesting was a page of class notes that he found inserted in the eugenics section of the textbook. Those notes give a rare insight into what a medical student at the time was being taught about the problems of genetics and what should be done about them.

According to the notes, after mentioning several eugenic proposals—including the need to control immigration to the United States to preserve the integrity of the nation's "good human stock" and the need to educate the masses on "sexual health"—the lecturer turned to legal issues concerning reproduction. Noted first is the need to control marriage by passing discriminating marriage laws. The lecturer apparently emphasized the need for laws that would prevent the marriage of people with epilepsy, insanity, or tuberculosis. A negative Wassermann test indicative of syphilis is also listed as a reason for denying a marriage license. In fact, many states passed restrictive marriage laws preventing marriages not only of people in these categories but also between people of different races. Miscegenation, or mixing of the races, it was argued, would result in inferior offspring. Miscegenation laws were not declared unconstitutional until the 1960s.

The medical student's notes go on to the subject of sterilization:

> Sterilization of defectives. This is the greatest remedy. The cutting of the vas deferens in the male & ligation or cutting of the tubes in the female. Does not interfere with individuals' happiness. Political cry goes up of "class legislation"?! [But] has been decided by the U.S. Supreme Court (Buck vs Bell) . . . . The country in an emergency may require an individual to give up his life, there is nothing inconsistent in asking for less.

This was the view expressed in the majority opinion of the Court in this decision—that the sacrifice of someone's reproductive rights for the greater good of all was not too much to ask for. Writing for the majority, Oliver Wendell Holmes referred to compulsory vaccination as necessary to protect others against the transmission of disease, and drew a parallel with compulsory sterilization as a reasonable requirement to protect others against the transmission of social and moral threats. He further argued that compulsory sterilization was best for the class of people most affected because it was more humane than the punishments that those born defective would eventually receive for their antisocial acts.

The expansion during the first half of this century of institutions for people classified as mentally retarded and mentally ill was rationalized in the same way: Institutionalization was best both for the people who were institutionalized and for society. Some even argued that mentally disabled people had a "right" to be institutionalized. In 1916, Joseph Mastin, the secretary of the Virginia Board of Charities and Corrections, wrote an article for the *Journal of Psycho-Asthenics* entitled "The New Colony Plan for the Feeble-Minded," in which he asserted:

> The right of the defective, then, is not the right to live as he pleases, but the right to live the fullest life possible under proper guidance. But the right is just as sacred as our own and we must see that he has it; to deny it is a social crime as well as a violation of the commandment, "Thou shalt love thy neighbor as thyself."
>
> . . . Therefore, while mental defectives are clearly not entitled to the rights of normal persons, it is indisputable that society is under obligations to give them such training as may be suited to their needs and capacities. . . .
>
> . . . As a rule, mental defectives are descended from the poorer classes, and for generations their people have lived in homes having few conveniences. To expect them to be contented in a great city institution with its up-to-date furnishings and equipment, and its strict routine, is unreasonable. They find little comfort in steam heat and polished floors; and the glare of our electric lights too often adds to their restlessness.
>
> . . . when the State shall demand that those in charge of her degenerate and helpless people shall see that they live happy and useful lives and that procreation by them is rendered impossible: then we can look forward with confidence to the coming of an era when feeble-mindedness will become extinct, mental disease will vanish and crime and pauperism will be reduced to a minimum.

> Then, and not until then, shall we get a clearer vision of the new heaven and the new earth wherein dwelleth **righteousness.**

The growth of institutions for people classified as mentally disabled was dramatic from the turn of the century through the 1950s. More institutions and larger institutions came to characterize state programs for the care of the mentally retarded and the mentally ill. Unfortunately, however, these institutions also became repositories for people whose disabilities did not really require that they be institutionalized. The institutions were available, convenient places to put people who might have been able to live more independently out in society but who required more attention or help than the average citizen. Of course, as more spaces were created in institutions, more people were found to fill them. And as more people came, more spaces were created. Not only were people with mild disabilities that did not require confinement sent to institutions, but so were people who were not mentally handicapped at all. As I have discussed in my book *Minds Made Feeble,* American society in the early twentieth century took note of what appeared to be growing numbers of vagrants, criminals, prostitutes, alcoholics, and other social undesirables. Their negative traits were seen as evidence of their mental deficiency, and authorities decided that such people needed to be hidden away from the rest of society. In many cases, people who were simply unwanted by anyone—people who were social nuisances in some way, who were alone and without advocates to protect them—found themselves in institutions. Sometimes they were inaccurately assigned a diagnostic label of mental retardation or mental illness; sometimes the formality of assigning a diagnosis was not even observed. I have reviewed many records of people who were admitted to institutions for the mentally retarded, who lived there for decades, and whose files designated them as "not retarded." The staff of the institutions, and sometimes the residents themselves, knew that the residents were there simply because they were unwanted; they were surplus persons whom society had decided to warehouse, again, in the name of protection: protection of society from the "deviant," and protection of the vulnerable deviant from the harsh realities of competitive social living.

Data included in the 1984 *International Review of Research in Mental Retardation* show the dramatic increase in the numbers of people who were institutionalized during this period. In a chapter entitled "Community Adjustment," Craig and McCarver show that in 1900 the average resident population in U.S. institutions for people diagnosed as mentally retarded was 300. By 1920 that figure was 600. By 1940 it had again doubled, to 1200. In 1950 the average was 1500 persons.

Colonies, training schools, hospitals, developmental centers—whatever they were called—became closed institutions, sometimes referred to as "total institutions." They were often intentionally self-sufficient, raising their own crops, operating their own dairies, sewing their own clothes. They were almost always walled off from the rest of society. Doors and gates were locked. At many institutions, there were bars on the doors and windows, restraining devices on the walls, and slots in doors for the passing of food trays. Those in charge of institutions of this era did not seem to know whether they were operating hospitals or prisons or something in between. The residents, who were called patients but who were often dressed more like inmates, seemed clearer about the nature of the institutions they occupied. Most learned to play the game and to survive as best they could, finding in the routine and predictability of these places at least a sense of certainty.

That sense of certainty ended for hundreds of thousands of people with mental disabilities beginning in the 1970s. With the national movement that became known as deinstitutionalization came the clearing out of people with mental retardation and mental illnesses from institutions. The impact of this movement would prove as dramatic as that of the expansion in institutionalization earlier in the century. The same source quoted earlier, from the *International Review of Research in Mental Retardation,* shows that by 1980 the average occupancy of institutions for people diagnosed as mentally retarded had dropped from a peak of 1500 in 1950 to 400 persons per institution. In 1989, three researchers at the University of Minnesota, C. C. White, K. C. Lakin, and R. H. Bruininks, reported that between 1967 and 1988, the deinstitutionalization movement resulted in a 58% reduction in the average daily population of people with mental retardation living in state-operated institutions in the United States.

The primary goal of the movement—to help people who do not really require institutional care to live as normally as possible in local communities—was admirable, one I believed in and supported as a teacher, graduate student, and professor. Most advocates for the rights and welfare of people with mental disabilities still embrace it. The goal sounds wonderful, it sounds like a cure for the institutional ills of the past. Indeed, when deinstitutionalization has been undertaken with proper planning, preparation, and resources, it has resulted in much fuller, freer, and more decent lives for those released. Too often, however, two mistakes have marred the deinstitutionalization process: First, financial and service resources have often not followed people from institutions to the community. The dollars used for years to house, feed, clothe, and otherwise care for people in institutions did not follow them in proportional amounts to support their transition to life in local communities. As for services, in most cases, community support services were created to serve the needs that had been being met in segregated institutional settings. State governments employed social workers, psychologists, and other professionals to assist mentally disabled people in community placements but never in adequate numbers. Over the past two decades, I have consistently seen competent and caring professionals stretched to the limit by case loads that are impossible to manage. And the low salary levels for these positions make attracting and keeping trained and experienced personnel very difficult. I have also known fine people dedicated to improving the lives of persons with disabilities in the community against all odds. They have worked for low salaries under often adverse circumstances with little recognition, and they have made all the difference in the lives of those for whom they advocate. They have been truly heroic in their efforts, and my admiration for them is immense.

The other flaw in the deinstitutionalization movement was that not enough was done at the state and national levels to develop appropriate places in communities for those leaving institutions to live. In recent years there has been much discussion about those deinstitutionalized people who now constitute a significant portion of the population designated as "homeless." Homelessness is a national tragedy and as such deserves our attention and care. Much has been written about the "problem" of the homeless, and not enough has been said about the individual human lives that constitute this "problem." Jonathan Kozol's book *Rachel and Her Children* is an exception to the silence. An important aspect of Kozol's findings is that many of those living on the streets are *not* mentally handicapped, drug addicted, or on the streets by choice. On the contrary, he found many families who had simply lost the economic struggle that has come to characterize contemporary American life. Kozol has contributed much to our understanding of the tragedy of homelessness. Nonetheless, we need to recognize that a significant number of the people living on the streets of our country did, in fact, at one time live in so-called mental institutions in states across our nation. The legions of homeless people who occupy the streets of our cities include former residents of mental health facilities and of mental retardation facilities. Two excellent sources of insight on this aspect of deinstitutionalization are *Out of Bedlam: The Truth About Deinstitutionalization* by A. B. Johnson and *Madness in the Streets: How Psychiatry and the Law Abandoned the Mentally Ill* by R. J. Isaac and V. C. Armat.

Given the focus of this book, however, on examining the effect of social policy through the life experiences of John Lovelace, I think it is important to look at what deinstitutionalization meant at the facility from which John was reintroduced to the community after twenty-five years of institutional life. My colleague Dr. Ed Polloway at Lynchburg College and I are currently analyzing more than 2300 discharge records from the Central Virginia Training Center from 1969 through 1989, hoping to discover patterns in the ages of those discharged, their levels of retardation, the length of their institutionalization, and other factors that may reflect changes in national and state laws, policies, and professional trends.

When we look at all of the discharges for that twenty-one-year period as a whole, we see that the word *deinstitutionalization* is a misnomer for about 40% of the people who left the institution. Though these people may have eventually found their way to another setting, their initial discharge was to other institutions—regional mental retardation centers, psychiatric facilities, or geriatric facilities—that were state operated. Nearly 2% of those officially discharged during this period were classified as "escapees"—people who disappeared while on parole or furlough, and were thereby lost to the system. I suspect that many of these people found better lives in the community on their own. Fewer than 0.5% of those discharged were released to the criminal justice system, having been, for the most part, convicted of crimes while on parole or furlough or during an escape from the institution. Another 30% of the people who left the Central Virginia Training Center between 1969 and 1989 were discharged to their own care or that of their families, usually with little evidence of a bridge of care or preparation. Some were sent off to communities with little done to prepare either them for the community or the community for them.

About 15% of the institution's discharged residents actually went into government-sponsored and community-based programs and facilities. These included group homes, halfway houses, intermediate care facilities (intermediate here meaning a level of care intermediate between institutionalization and community living), supervised apartments, work training programs, and foster homes.

Finally, almost 13% of those leaving the institution between 1969 and 1989 were discharged to private, and primarily profit-driven, adult homes or nursing homes. And certainly, many more found their way to these for-profit adult and nursing homes after an initial stop in one of the other placements already described. During this period, adult homes became a growth industry. Unfortunately, they also became a dumping ground for unwanted people of every description and diagnosis. Visiting these homes, I have consistently found them, as I mentioned earlier, to be populated by a mixture of people who are elderly, mentally retarded, mentally disabled, otherwise damaged, alone, or a combination thereof. Often, the common denominator is that they are simply poor, weak, unwanted, and unable to defend themselves against a social environment that wants them out of the way.

And so John Lovelace left the institution that had become his home, the place where he knew how to survive, and where he had a few friends among the staff. He left for environments where he would fare worse. As we've seen, his behavior would deteriorate and each new placement would be a step down the ladder for him. He finally found himself living in a "home" with 200 other unwanted people where his very life would be considered not worth saving. Deinstitutionalization and community placement did not work for John, and I fear his history—his insufficient chance to "live and work . . . just like all other men in our country"—is one shared by thousands of others.

Because of my interest in the history of the treatment of people classified as mentally retarded, I have several times over the years discussed with friends and colleagues the motivations of people who were involved in actions that now seem shameful in the harm they caused to people who deserved better. Were those people who led the movement to expand institutions, and who worked to remove more and more people from society because of perceived defects, calloused toward the humanity of those whom they sought to commit to those institutions? Were those who wrote and implemented involuntary sterilization laws in this country fascists? Of course not. Both of these causes were taken up by people with the best of personal and philosophical intentions. Many of those who advocated involuntary sterilization also spoke out strongly for more equitable treatment of members of racial and ethnic minorities. Some were ahead of their time in calling for greater social equality for women. Among those who helped promote the institutionalization of people with mental retardation were recognized humanitarians and philanthropists. The damage done to people by needless institutionalization and unjustified sterilization was not intended by these people but happened, nonetheless. I am sure that some of these advocates would have been shocked at the consequences of their movements had they lived long enough to see the ultimate results. I am also sure that some who did live long enough to see the results were shocked.

I have been asked on occasion what I think history will say of us who in recent years have been critical of earlier approaches to the treatment of mental retardation. I have come to believe that ultimately history will find us at fault for carrying out a good idea badly. I think history will show that in many cases deinstitutionalization was a banner under which many who continued to need help were politically and economically abandoned. I think we will be found lacking in our vigilance over a process that needed to be watched very closely.

Chapter 10

John Lovelace and the Mercantile Theory of Mental Retardation

By the time I learned that the no-code order for John Lovelace had been rescinded, he had already been discharged from the Burrell Home for Adults. Apparently, the case manager employed by the community services board in Roanoke who was officially responsible for monitoring John's status and well-being had been contacted by the social worker at the Burrell Home and informed that a new living arrangement would have to be found for him right away. Fortunately, the placement she arranged for John was a move in the right direction. (I say "fortunately" because my impression from subsequent conversations with her was that she was carefully providing John the services that she was required to provide and nothing more—though in fairness to her I must say that she may have been less than enthusiastic speaking to me because she'd been told that I was "meddling" and "making trouble" concerning John.)

John had been moved to an adult home called the Little Ponderosa, located a few miles east of Roanoke near the small town of Bonsak. The Little Ponderosa houses about twenty men in a large old country house with an annex. When I first visited there, I was struck with how much more pleasant it was than the Burrell Home. The annex, where most of the men lived, had a large porch, and there was a large yard with fruit trees and flowering bushes. The atmosphere here was simply much more pleasant and inviting than I had seen at the several other adult homes I had visited up to then. The Little Ponderosa was managed by one of the owners, Bob Williams, whom I met on my first visit there. Throughout John's stay at the Little Ponderosa, Bob Williams was always open to my questions about John's life there, and was always willing to cooperate with me as I tried to help John meet some of his basic needs. From the first, he impressed me with both his knowledge about the business of running an adult home and his quiet respect for the consumers of his services. He truly seemed to like the men, and they to like him.

Most, perhaps even all, of the other residents of the Little Ponderosa had a diagnosis of mental illness rather than mental retardation. By this time, John himself had been labeled schizophrenic, in the course of a psychiatric consultation that came about because of his behavioral and social difficulties. Though I do not think this diagnosis was accurate, I am glad for the error, in that it probably contributed to John's placement at the Little Ponderosa.

John was different from the other men at the Little Ponderosa in another regard. Most, again perhaps all, of the others were disabled veterans. They were therefore entitled to Veterans Administration benefits, which far exceed the benefits paid to other disabled people. During my visits, I also had the impression that most of the other men still had family and friendship ties far stronger than I have observed in other adult homes.

I visited John at the Little Ponderosa shortly after learning that he had been moved there. He seemed to be proud to show me around and introduced me to several people as his friend. I enjoyed sitting with him on the porch of the main house, rocking in rocking chairs and looking out over the lawn of this old frame home. How relieved I was to find John in this friendlier, more serene environment.

Sitting with John there on the porch, I asked him for the first time about his family. At this point, I had not yet begun to look into his background and I knew little about his life before he came to the Burrell Home. I had to listen closely to his comments about his early life, because I had, and still have, difficulty at times understanding his speech. I frequently asked him to repeat himself or to speak more loudly. I know that this became annoying to him after a while, but he persisted in trying to tell me his story. My conversation with John that afternoon convinced me even more that his abilities had been underestimated over the years. It also made me more sensitive to how frustrating it must have been throughout most of his life for John to have such difficulty making himself understood to others.

Twice each day, Bob Williams took a vanload of men to a minimart a few miles from the Little Ponderosa. On one of my visits, I went along. The men rode quietly to the market and had little to say while shopping, walking straight to the coffeepots, the soft drink coolers, and the snack shelves as soon as they entered the store. Taking their selections to the counter, they asked for packs of cigarettes to add to their purchases. One man even bought a carton. John had only a small amount of change with him. I told him that I wanted to treat him to something and asked what he would like. His reply was no surprise to me: He wanted a large cup of coffee and some cigarettes. I paid for both while he poured his coffee. (As a reformed smoker, I always had mixed feelings at buying John cigarettes: I know they do him harm. On the other hand, I understand his addiction and realize that smoking is one of the few pleasures he has. So, though I have tried to vary the kinds of gifts I give him for birthdays, Christmas, and other occasions, my buying him cigarettes has become a part of our relationship. As guilty as I feel about the act, it is cigarettes and cigarette money that he most appreciates.)

What became most clear to me from this visit to the minimart with John and the other men was the difference between the discretionary resources available to the others and the money that John had for his personal use. John had a monthly allowance of thirty dollars for all of his personal expenses. This money was to cover everything other than his room and board and whatever other maintenance and care the home might provide. The combined funding from Social Security disability benefits and Virginia supplementary benefits for his care came to $521 per month, paid directly to the Little Ponderosa, just as it had been earlier to the Burrell Home. This was the standard amount of funding provided for adult home care of disabled people with no income or other resources available to them. That figure has not increased substantially today. This translated into approximately seventeen dollars per day for John's housing, food, care, recreation, and a profit for the operator of the home. Obviously, the profit margin can be increased only by economizing as far as possible on housing, food, and staffing. I saw less evidence of this cost cutting at the Little Ponderosa than I have seen elsewhere—perhaps in part because the veterans who lived there were eligible for more funding.

I do not know how much personal money the Veterans Administration provided the disabled veterans at the Little Ponderosa. I have been told that it varies with the degree of disability and other variables that are factored into a formula for determining benefits. Many of these men also received money from their families or from other sources. Whatever the source, their resources contrasted dramatically with John's thirty dollars a month. This amount was expected to cover John's toiletries, clothing, entertainment, refreshments, and anything else he might need. In John's case, of course, almost every penny went for cigarettes and, even so, that amount was not nearly enough to keep him supplied all month.

The next few months seemed to go fairly smoothly for John at the Little Ponderosa. He appeared to be getting along well with the other residents. He was working several days each week at a nearby sheltered workshop. This work seemed particularly important to him as a source of extra money to meet his need for cigarettes.

It was during this time that I asked John to sign release forms so that I could look at his records—both those at what was now the Central Virginia Training Center and those kept by the Department of Social Services since his discharge. I also made several trips to the town where he had grown up to check on courthouse records and old newspapers in the public library. All of this information eventually came together to form the picture of John's life history as I have shared it here.

Over these months, I visited John several times at the Little Ponderosa. I usually walked around the grounds a bit with him, talked with Bob Williams about how things were going, and took John for a shopping trip to the minimart. Once, I took him a cardboard trunk full of clothing that I could no longer wear but that I thought would fit him. I also thought that we wore the same size shoes, and took him several pairs. Unfortunately, most of the clothing didn't fit or wasn't appropriate for the kind of laundering done at the Ponderosa. The shoes were too tight, and I found out later that John had traded one particularly nice pair for a pack of cigarettes.

During one of these visits, Bob Williams told me that he had received complaints from the sheltered workshop that John was coming to work with torn clothing and body odor. He also explained that the home could not provide John deodorant and new clothing, though Bob had given John a pair of his own used running shoes that John wore regularly for many months. It all came back, however, to the same bind. John had only thirty dollars each month, and all of it went for cigarettes. Though he was earning a little extra money now at the workshop, they wanted him to spend more on clothing and personal hygiene. The more you learn about how the system works for many disabled and poor people, the more "Catch 22s" become apparent. I bought John some deodorant, and we scratched together some better clothing. John and I also talked about the importance of his meeting the expectations and standards of the workshop so that he could continue working there. I hoped for the best.

On July 19, 1988, I received a call from Bob Williams. John had been sent home from the workshop in late June because of a temper tantrum. He would not be allowed to return. I talked with John a few days later, and he pleaded with me to help him get his job back. He was very upset at losing his means of extra income. He couldn't really explain what had happened when he was terminated, but he assured me that if he had another chance he would control his behavior. I wrote to the director of the workshop, asking about the incident that had led to John's termination while trying to frame my inquiry with fairness to the people at the workshop, who I was certain had made a difficult decision in John's case.

> I talked with Mr. Bob Williams of Little Ponderosa recently concerning John Lovelace. He explained that John was terminated from involvement at Tinker Mountain Industries in late June. It is my understanding that John was terminated because of a temper tantrum, and consequent aggressive and hostile behavior.
>
> I have known John Lovelace for about a year and a half. During that time I have come to feel a responsibility to him as a friend/advocate. I would appreciate any further description you could give me concerning the circumstances of John's separation from Tinker Mountain.
>
> Please understand that I am not questioning the action which has been taken. I simply need to have a better insight on what is happening in John's life at this time. I am on the Board of Directors of Lynchburg Sheltered Industries and I fully comprehend that difficult decisions must be made about individuals in light of the best interests of the overall organization.
>
> Thank you for your assistance with this matter. I hope you are having a pleasant summer.

I received a courteous reply from the sheltered workshop indicating their willingness to help me understand the circumstances of John's termination there. Before they would share any information with me, however, I had to have John sign a release form. I had become accustomed to this requirement by then and did the necessary paperwork. With time required for everything to be processed, though, it was early August before I knew the exact circumstances of John's dismissal from the workshop. I received a long letter of explanation from the woman who had followed John's case most closely there.

> John began his latest employment with Tinker Mountain Industries on March 22, 1988. The agreement was that John was to work two days a week. . . . John did not keep to the agreement

and began coming every day. When he was here every day, John was often verbally abusive to staff as well as his co-workers. I discussed the behaviors with John on several occasions. He agreed that he would try to do better.

April 21, 1988 Mr. Williams from Little Ponderosa telephoned me about John's behavior at home. We agreed that five days a week for John seemed to be too much. After much discussion with John and Mr. Williams, John agreed to work on Mondays, Tuesdays, and Fridays beginning April 26, 1988. During this time John's behavior became worse. He was grouchy and looked tired. He asked about returning to work five days a week whenever he was here. John did not understand that we were concerned about his health and his well-being. John said that he wanted to work in order to obtain more money.

A minor problem with John was that he often had bad body odor. John was informed that in order to keep working at TMI he must bathe and wear appropriate clothing to work. A telephone call was made to Little Ponderosa stating the same. John's clothing was often torn and dirty.

On June 20, 1988 John came to me asking that he be allowed to work five days a week. I explained that his behavior on this day had been unacceptable. He had already yelled at his supervisor for not being able to bring him more work right away. Later in the afternoon, John yelled at his co-worker for not bringing him work. [John was doing piece work. The more items he completed each day the more he earned.] He proceeded to throw a box of work on the floor. When counseled about his behavior, John stated that he couldn't make any money working three days a week. He apologized for his previous behavior and said that he would try not to be angry but talk with his case manager instead.

Approximately five minutes later, John literally threw work at another employee. He balled up his fist to hit him. If I had not told John at that point not to, he would have hit him. John was asked to come to my office to calm down. He threw his glasses on the floor. Another case manager picked up his glasses for him.

> John got out of the chair and hit the wall as he walked out of the room.
>
> It was at this point that TMI staff called Little Ponderosa. We asked that someone pick him up immediately. John was asked to stay in the cafeteria. John threw a chair and he attempted to push over a floor fan. John was then asked to go outside. We felt that if he smoked a cigarette he would feel better. Once outside John calmed down some. He said that he had to work five days a week. The rehabilitation manager and I explained that we were concerned about his health and behaviors such as those he had exhibited on this day. It was explained to John that he was suspended from work for two days. He was told there was a possibility of termination.
>
> . . . [A] meeting was held to discuss John's case. It was the decision of the group that he would be terminated due to poor health and aggressive behaviors toward clients as well as staff.
>
> Professor Smith, I have tried to enclose all of the particulars of John's separation from TMI. Please notify me if there is other information needed. I have also enclosed several incident reports and a progress report for your information.

The incident reports documented what the letter described. John had repeatedly lashed out at others at the workshop, exploding when he felt that his "livelihood" was in jeopardy. He wanted to work five days a week to make more money, but his attempts at protecting his income resulted only in losses.

I wrote back to the workshop expressing my understanding of their actions. Indeed, John had become a threat to the well-being of the staff and other clients there. They had given him repeated chances to redeem himself, but he had been unable to do so.

A satire I once read on some of the exotic theories of mental retardation that have been developed over the years described in burlesque detail what the author called the mercantile theory of mental retardation. After having come to understand some of the dilemmas John faced, I find some truth in this satire. Indeed, his life has been most handicapped by his inability to secure the resources to meet his own needs. His frustrations and difficulties have, more often than not, arisen from his inability to produce and earn his own way to his own goals. I expect that this is a common experience for many who are labeled mentally retarded. Being mentally retarded can thus be seen as not being a part of the economic and social system: being outside of the commerce of life and, therefore, having no value to that system. The experience of being a surplus person is one that many mentally retarded people share, along with others who, because of age, background, or other disability, are viewed as having no value.

Chapter 11

To: John Lovelace From: "Your Friends"

The summer of 1988 was long and frustrating for John. He was no longer working at the workshop, and he had little to do with his time. In addition, his glasses were broken. They had survived the toss he gave them in anger at the workshop, but the frames were broken when he accidentally sat on them on his bed one morning. After the frames were broken, a lens was misplaced. I had a call from Bob Williams explaining the situation. John would be able to get replacements through the community services board in Roanoke, but the wait would probably be several months. Bob also reported that John acted as if he were blind without his glasses, literally needing to be guided from place to place. This was the first time I realized how poor John's vision had become.

I told Bob that I would give the matter some thought and get back to him soon. I was troubled by how disabled John was without his glasses and by the long delay involved in getting him help through the state system. I was so frustrated that I almost called Bob back immediately to tell him to schedule an appointment for John at my expense. I had no idea what the cost would be but guessed that the lenses would be expensive. One other possibility occurred to me, however, before I called Bob. My friend Bill Hadden is an active member of the Lions Club, an organization that has long made projects of sight conservation and services to blind people. I gave Bill a call and explained the situation to him. Before I hung up, I had his assurance that the Lions would pay for both the examination and the glasses, and an address to which the charges could be billed. Soon John had new glasses—for which I am still grateful to Bill Hadden and the Lions of Virginia.

During this time, I contacted the Department of Social Services in Martinsville, the town where John had been born and had grown up, and where he had been placed when he was first discharged from the Lynchburg Training School. I asked them to allow me to review John's records—after, of course, another round of the release forms to which I had become so accustomed.

John's records showed that his "freedom" in the adult home to which he had initially been discharged lasted less than a year. After fighting with another resident, who lost two teeth in the confrontation, John was removed briefly, as discussed earlier. Before the year was up, he was sent to another facility, a larger home. John lived there for two years, working at a workshop nearby until he was terminated and then discharged from the home. He was then sent to an adult home in Roanoke, where he lived for two years, working at Tinker Mountain Industries. He was then transferred to another adult home in Roanoke for less than a year. Finally, he found himself at the Burrell Home. His residency there would last less than two years and the events that brought John to my attention would occur during this time. Besides these records, John's folder contained a curious entry indicating that, at about the time the no-code order was issued at Burrell, a call had been made to Social Services in Martinsville to report that John had a brain tumor and was not expected to live. I interpreted this as yet another indication of the degree to which John had been written off.

While visiting in Martinsville, I became acquainted with a social worker who had been responsible in part for processing the forms necessary for John's disability benefits to be paid to the various adult homes he had lived in since leaving Lynchburg. John was just a name to her, as she had never met him, but when I had occasion to talk with her at length, she listened with interest to John's story, and seemed genuinely moved by what I shared with her.

Two days before Christmas that year, I visited John to deliver a card and a small gift. After we had talked and he had opened his gift, he eagerly showed me a package he had received the day before from his "hometown." The tag read simply, "From your friends in Martinsville." Beautifully wrapped and neatly packed, the box contained some nice used clothing (a jacket, two sweaters, and several pairs of pants), new clothing (several pairs of underwear and socks), deodorant and other toiletries, a large can of roasted peanuts, and a nice card that was again signed only "friends." Obviously moved by the gift, John was especially touched that it came from people in his hometown of Martinsville.

Knowing, of course, that the gifts had come from the social worker in Martinsville, I wrote to her on Christmas and thanked her, for John and for me, for the special joy that she had brought to this holiday. She truly had, I thought, brought the spirit of Christmas alive with her caring expression of charity and concern. When I saw her several weeks later, she thanked me but then took me aside to ask me not to mention to anyone that she had sent the gifts. She explained that one of the reasons that she had signed the card and tag "friends" was that agency regulations prohibited employees from becoming "personally involved" with clients. She was afraid that if her gifts to John became known, she could be found in violation of agency rules! I assured her that I would protect her anonymity.

On January 24, Bob Williams called to tell me that he had fired the Little Ponderosa's "night man"—essentially a night watchman who did a bit of cleaning while the residents slept. Bob had fired the night man because John complained that the man had kicked him. After investigating a bit, Bob found John's complaint to be true. John had a cut and a bruise, and another man had witnessed the kick. Bob said that there was some confusion concerning the circumstances. The night man claimed that John went into a shouting tantrum when he would not give him a cigarette. Bob's response was that, regardless of the circumstances, the man had violated the Ponderosa's standards by reacting to John with physical force. Though Bob apologized several times for the man's actions, I was left at the end of our conversation with the sad sense that things were beginning to fall apart again in John's life.

In less than a week I had another call from Bob. John had continued to have temper outbursts. When Bob tried to talk with John about these episodes, he could get little out of him except that John wanted to go back to work. But the response of the case manager at the Roanoke community services office was unequivocal: In Bob's words, John had been "written off when it comes to work; there is no chance." And Bob himself no longer felt that he could continue to have John live at the Little Ponderosa. He felt that John's disability and life situation differed so much from those of the other men there that the arrangement simply wasn't going to work.

Bob did suggest another living arrangement for John. He explained that he was the part owner of another adult home, the Draper Valley Rest Home, located in a little village about fifty miles west of Roanoke. He described the facility to me and explained that more of the residents there were mentally retarded. He also said that the community services case managers there had been very helpful in arranging employment for the residents at a sheltered workshop nearby. He assured me that the facility was actually nicer than the Little Ponderosa and that John would have a semiprivate room there instead of the bunk-style arrangement he had currently. Bob seemed to be seeking my blessing for transferring John to Draper Valley. He was very positive in his conversation with me, but it was also obvious that John's time at the Little Ponderosa had come to an end and the alternative that Bob was offering was the only one readily available. For what it was worth, I gave my "blessing." Within days, the appropriate social services agency documents had been executed and John was on his way to Draper Valley Rest Home.

Soon after John's move, and before I had had a chance to visit him in his new home, I wrote to the administrator of Draper Valley, Frances Martin, whom Bob had spoken of very highly.

> I am a friend and advocate for John Lovelace. Bob Williams may have mentioned that I try to watch out for John's best interests. I hope that he is doing well in his new home.
>
> I also hope that by now John has been able to start to work at the sheltered workshop. I know that he will be much happier being able to work each day. I understand that there will be recreational programs available for John.
>
> Please read this letter to him after you finish with it and give it to him to keep.
>
> John, I hope that you like your new home. It sounds very nice. I look forward to seeing you at Camp Virginia Jaycee on March 31.

John Lovelace at Camp Virginia Jaycee (Courtesy of the Roanoke Times and World-News)

Bob Williams should be getting the information about the camp weekend real soon.

I hope you have started working or will real soon. Please remember the importance of getting along with everyone there as best as you can. I am hoping that you will be very happy living in Draper.

Take care. I will see you soon.

On the same day that I wrote this letter, I also wrote to the head of the Mormon Church of Latter-Day Saints in Lynchburg, whom I had met some years before. Mrs. Hunter, John's foster mother, had been a member of the Mormon Church and had taken him to church regularly; some of his old records at the Lynchburg Training School and Hospital had even listed his religion as being Mormon. I had contacted the church leader earlier explaining some things about John's life and current circumstances, and asking that the Mormon congregation in Roanoke be informed about John. I hoped that they would take an interest in him and visit him, giving him some ties in the community, and easing his loneliness. Members of the Roanoke church had, indeed, visited him, read to him, and brought him presents.

My letter explained his move and appealed for continued contact:

Thank you so much for your help with John Lovelace. Members of the Mormon Church visited with him at the Little Ponderosa, and I know it meant a great deal to him to have this contact with the Church he grew up with in Martinsville.

There is, however, a bit of a complication to the contact established with John. He is now living in a different facility. He was recently moved to the Draper Valley Rest Home near Radford. The living arrangement there is better for John and there is a sheltered workshop nearby where he will be able to work each day.

I know that John would appreciate having visitors from the Mormon Church in his new home. Would you please arrange for a congregation near Blacksburg or Radford to make contact with him?

I also wrote to the social worker in Martinsville about John's move. I assumed that she might have seen or executed some of the paperwork involved, and I encouraged her continued personal, but anonymous, interest in John. I hoped that his "friends" in Martinsville would continue to remember him at special times.

It was around this same time that I made another decision aimed at connecting John with communities that might help, encourage, or protect him. I mentioned earlier the work of journalist Mike Hudson. Mike had been working for many months on a series of articles about adult homes for the *Roanoke Times and World News*. I had learned of his research and the planned series through my friend Mary Bishop, a brilliant and compassionate reporter who was a finalist for a Pulitzer Prize in 1989 and who had written two stories on the issue of involuntary sexual sterilization.

I had asked for Mary's advice on several occasions as I tried to find ways to be a friend to John. It occurred to me after a while that if John's story were made public in some way, two things might result: First, making the no-code incident public might help ensure that such would never happen again—to John or to anyone else in the same circumstances. Second, I hoped that a newspaper account of John's life might spark interest from someone or some organization that could offer him some support.

With this in mind, I invited Mary to lunch one day and dumped a pile of information about John in her lap—material I had gathered from the Lynchburg Training School records and other sources. I asked her to look it over to see if she would be willing to write John's story for the newspaper. She promised to give it serious consideration.

When I next heard from Mary, she suggested that we meet with Mike Hudson and Rich Martin, the editor they both worked with, as she really felt that John's story belonged with Mike's series on adult homes. She felt that it would be better understood in this context and that it would receive more attention. She had also been impressed with the thoroughness and care Mike was giving to the series. She was confident that he would be just as conscientious about John's story.

When we met with Mike and Rich, they explained that John's story would follow two or three days of major articles on adult homes and the people who live in them. They were excited about the human face that John's life story would bring to the series. As the meeting progressed, I became more confident that the story would be in good hands. Though I could not ask for editorial privileges, of course, Mike offered to let me read a draft of the story before it was published. He also asked if we could visit John together before he wrote the story. We left with a tentative understanding that Mike could do the story, but that I had to speak with John before we proceeded further. I did so later that week, explaining the idea of the newspaper story as best I could. He readily agreed, but once again, I think that he agreed out of friendship rather than with any real grasp of the significance of the story. I called Mike to tell him that he could write the story, and we arranged to visit John together.

John's story was published in the *Roanoke Times and World News* on October 5, 1989. It was a front-page story with a large color photograph of John sitting on his bed at the Draper Valley Rest Home. The story opened with a description of John's birth and early life in Martinsville. A detailed description of his life at the Lynchburg Training School and Hospital followed, and then came the discussion of his deinstitutionalization after twenty years there:

> Two decades later, the state institution spat him back out into the world—into Virginia's adult home system.
>
> He's been there ever since. Like many other mentally disabled people who live in Virginia's adult homes, he's been poor, lonely and unwanted.
>
> He is now 59, with a deeply furrowed forehead and streaks of gray in his black hair. He has a thin face, but his jowls are fleshy and hang down like a sad-eyed hound dog's. When he sits, he keeps his head hung low.
>
> Over the past decade, he has bounced from home to home. His second-hand clothes have been stuffed in battered dresser drawers, his toothbrush and soap stuffed in a Ziploc plastic bag like a makeshift travel kit.
>
> Sometimes he's worked in sheltered workshops and had a few dollars in his pocket. But often he hasn't, and in his frustration and loneliness he's struck out at others, throwing chairs and punches.
>
> It was by accident two years ago that John Lovelace found a friend—and advocate.

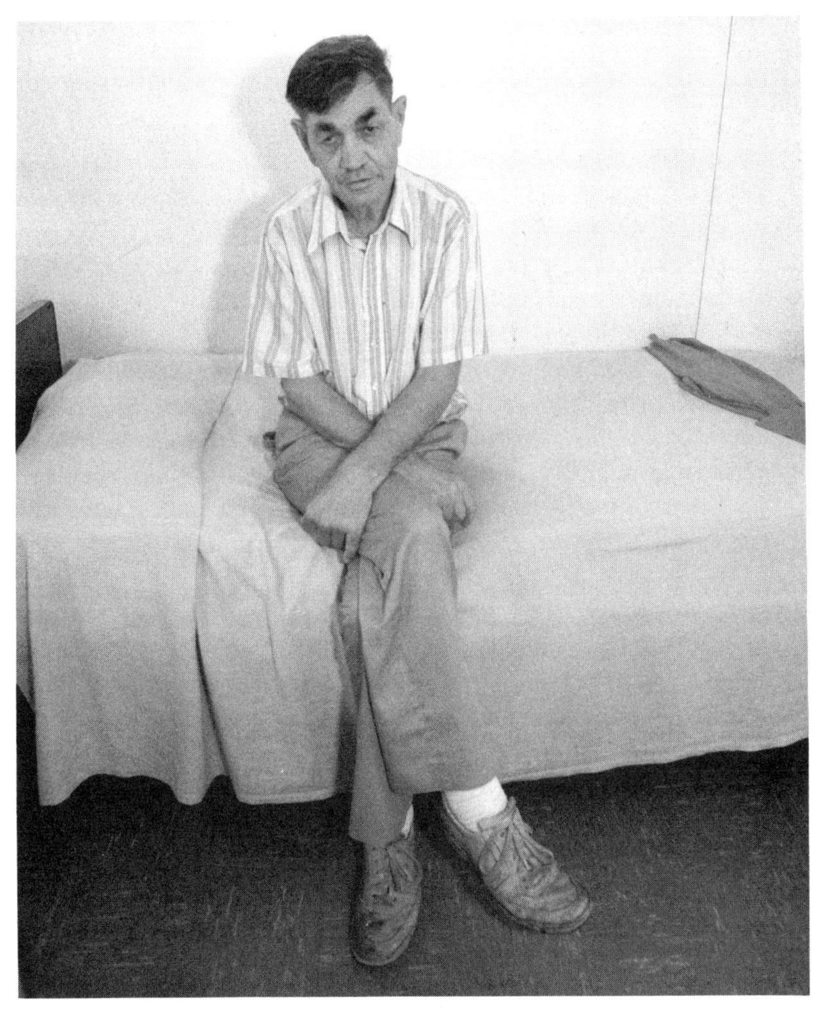

John Lovelace at Draper Valley Rest Home (Courtesy of the Roanoke Times and World-News)

J. David Smith, a Lynchburg College professor, stumbled onto Lovelace at Camp Virginia Jaycee, a camp for the handicapped in Bedford County.

Smith, who had a group of students there as volunteers, noticed something unusual in Lovelace's file. A doctor's report from Burrell

> Home for Adults included a "No Code" order for Lovelace—meaning that no one should try to save his life if he had a brain hemorrhage or other medical emergency.
>
> It upset Smith because "No Code" orders are usually reserved for people who are dying or comatose and kept alive by machines.
>
> It seemed to Smith to suggest that Lovelace's "very life was viewed as not worth living."
>
> For Smith, who has written three books about the retarded, it was another example of what happens when a retarded person doesn't have an advocate to fight for him.
>
> "The vision and the dream of the deinstitutionalization movement really turn sour for a lot of people like John," he said. "I think John's whole life illustrates the tragedy of being an unwanted, surplus person."
>
> Whether it's been in a state institution or an adult home, "the end result is still the same—he's very alone in life."

Mike's article continued with an account of John's years at the Lynchburg Training School and Hospital and the circumstances of his discharge. It listed the homes that he had lived in since he was deinstitutionalized, and the unfortunate circumstances that had led to his leaving each of them, right up to his departure from the Little Ponderosa. The article concluded with a description of John's current situation:

> After that, he moved to Draper Valley Rest Home in Pulaski County with the hope of getting into a sheltered workshop in the New River Valley.
>
> He's still waiting, but his chances are looking better, Frances Martin, the home's administrator, said.
>
> A change in his medication and the attention from Smith seem to have helped Lovelace control his temper better, she said. "He comes up to me and says, 'You proud of me?' And I'll say, 'Yes I am.' "
>
> Lovelace said he wasn't sure why he sometimes gets angry. But, he said, "I holding it in."
>
> When Smith visited him a few weeks ago, Lovelace told him: "Dave, I want to get my own money."

He gets a $30-a-month allowance out of the state welfare grant that pays for his care, but that goes quickly for cigarettes and sodas.

Smith took him to a country store and bought him four packs of Marlboros and four batteries for his AM/FM radio. The batteries didn't help because it turned out the radio was broken.

Mostly, Lovelace spends his days sleeping, sitting on the porch with other residents or watching television. "They dance sometimes on TV," he said.

In the closet he shares with his roommate, there's a winter jacket he got at Christmas in a package marked, "From your friends in Martinsville." It was from a social worker who could not put her name on the box because she's not supposed to get personally involved.

He was pleased to get a gift from his home town. He hasn't heard from his kinfolk or foster family in years.

When Smith mentioned his foster mother, Lovelace said: "I don't have a foster mom. She's dead. A car kilt her."

Chapter 12

"Fairview Is Nice to Me"

My friendship with John Lovelace is one that I value greatly, for several reasons. First, I like him. He is a gentle, loving man who genuinely enjoys being with others when he is able to communicate and share with them—though, of course, he gets frustrated when he cannot make himself understood or when he has difficulty understanding others' words and intentions.

John's friendship is also important to me because it keeps me personally connected to the human services that are the focus of my professional and academic work. My knowing John constantly challenges me to think about the meaning of what I study and teach in terms of the life of my friend. I now advise my students to always have in their lives at least one person they are concerned about to whom they are not related in any way, and with whom they are not paid to be involved. I have come to believe that we all need this kind of relationship to keep alive our humanistic and altruistic impulses, and the motivation that originally brought many of us to working to serve other people. If we lose these values, we and those who depend on our advocacy and services suffer a great loss.

A third reason that John's friendship is so special to me is that it has taught me much about how slowly and reluctantly our human services system functions. I have been involved with education and rehabilitation programs for children and adults with disabilities for almost thirty years. I have four academic degrees in fields that are all related to the education, counseling, and rehabilitation of people with special needs. Over the years, I have established contacts with some of the world's most knowledgeable and influential people in these fields. I have taught hundreds of undergraduate and graduate students. I have been a consultant on scores of projects. Yet, in trying to help this one man in some very basic ways, I have been largely unsuccessful or have found the process painfully slow. My insider position has made little difference in the outcomes for John. As the preceding chapters illustrate, securing minimal changes in his life has taken years.

My friendship with John has thus given me new insights about the painful experiences that many families of persons with disabilities encounter. I have gained a deep appreciation for the constant struggle that these families face, though I still cannot imagine just how powerless and frustrated the mothers, fathers, siblings, and friends of people who are disabled must feel when they try to get help for those they love without the benefit of the preparation I have had. I think, too, that I now understand those who get worn down by the experience, those who give up, those who live with undeserved guilt, and those who abandon the hope that things can ever get better. I understand the bitterness and anger some feel toward the system, and toward individual teachers, therapists, and other representatives of the system. I think that through John I have come closer to grasping the special despair I have seen in families of disabled children, that sense of having been wronged by fate.

I had hoped that publication of the article about John would somehow make an immediate and profound difference in his life. The *Roanoke Times and World-News* is read throughout southwestern Virginia and is otherwise one of the state's most important newspapers. I expected dramatic results after the story appeared.

After more than six months at Draper Valley, John was still not working at the sheltered workshop, and no other program or service had been arranged for him. He seemed to be controlling his anger better, but nothing else was happening. The administrator seemed concerned, but it was not her role to arrange for services outside the adult home. John was still inaccurately classified as psychotic, which continued to cause confusion about who should be overseeing his case, and what services he needed or was qualified for. Repeated inquiries had brought

John Lovelace at Camp Virginia Jaycee with Friends

no progress. Some of the professionals I spoke with seemed confused as to who I was in relation to John, and why I was calling or writing in regard to him from more than a hundred miles away. I was frustrated. I think I expected that the article would be read by these same people and that it would bring recognition to John and legitimacy to my interest in him.

There is no doubt that Mike Hudson's series on adult homes made a difference. His articles were read around the state and raised interest in reforming the system. Mike is a fine journalist, and he did his job well. I trust that the interest that he stimulated among policy makers in Virginia will help lead to the kinds of changes that are needed. Among the general public, however, though the topic of adult homes captured a great deal of attention during the week that the series appeared, that attention quickly waned. For me, this was an important lesson in how fickle we are in our culture in our attention to the mass media. We focus on issues as they pass through our field of awareness, and then we quickly move on to the next hot topic. I sometimes wonder how the daily media bombardment we experience affects our commitment to staying with problems and people to some point of action.

I did not expect a flood of calls and letters to the newspaper asking how John Lovelace could be helped, but I did expect some. To my knowledge, there were none.

John was proud of the fact that he was in the newspaper. Frances Martin later told me that the photographs really impressed him. Overall, however, John took his few minutes of fame in stride. His dictated letter a few days later simply said:

> I am doing real good at Draper. I help with mopping and sweeping. I get extra cigs and pop for helping. I like doing that.
>
> I have received your letter and money. That came in handy. I go to the store every day.
>
> Mrs. Martin (we call her Frances) said she was proud of me. That I was her big helper. She always hugs and tells me I am doing good. She kisses us [and] tells us that she cares for us a lot. She gave me my pictures in the paper and the story. Sharon my friend is writting this letter for me. She writes for all of us. She lives upstairs.

Despite the lack of public response, however, the article did serve John in other ways. By December 1989, John still had not even been evaluated for the possibility of working at the sheltered workshop. He had not, in fact, been seen for placement in any sort of program or service. As far as I could determine, he was spending all of his time at Draper Valley dependent on the good graces of the staff, with no meaningful outside contact. Frustrated, I finally appealed to a friend within the state mental retardation system for help. He gave me the name of a person to write to with the agreement that I would not discuss this with anyone else. To honor that request I will delete his name from the letter that I reprint here. It was his assistance, however, that led the way to some important improvements in John's life.

I am writing to you at the suggestion of. . . . [He] speaks highly of you and felt you would be willing to try to help me with a concern that I have for a friend who is living at Draper Valley Rest Home. The enclosed article will give you background on John Lovelace and my relationship with him. I hope you can take the time to read it.

For close to a year I have been attempting to help John with at least a trial placement at the New River Valley Workshop. I know that having employment there would mean a great deal to him in terms of the quality of his daily life, his self-esteem and having at least some income. So far I have been frustrated in this attempt. For some reason John has been placed under mental health rather than mental retardation. I really think that this is inappropriate since his primary diagnosis has always been mental retardation. Anyway, I have practically begged for information and assistance with little in the way of results. Sometimes my calls have not even been returned. I am not a person who is quick to complain and I believe that I have been patient and courteous with the person I have had contact with. . . . I don't want to cause difficulty for her. I just want to give John the best possible chance at an improved life.

I would appreciate any assistance you might offer me. I know the holiday season is here and things are hectic. When you find time, however, would you please take a look at John's situation? Thanks in advance.

I was obviously frustrated by and tired of waiting for the improvements I had thought would follow John's move almost immediately. Instead, I had seen no movement toward his being allowed to work. I'm sure that similar letters have been written with far less satisfying results than I received. I was lucky: To my delight a former student of mine responded to my concerns. Good luck and interest generated by the article I had sent with my letter began to change John's life. The letter from my former student, Cathi Drinkard, proved to be a turning point:

Dear Dr. Smith:

My Director . . . recently received your letter of December 12, 1989, and brought it to my immediate attention during a meeting yesterday. I am most pleased to be able to assist you as you were of so much help to me during my graduate studies at Lynchburg College.

In regard to the matter that you addressed, allow me to explain what I have done so far. I have contacted Mr. Lovelace's Mental Health worker to ascertain why he is in their system instead of ours. It appears that when Mr. Lovelace came to Draper Valley Rest Home, no documentation accompanied him. Therefore, when his case was opened on July 5, 1988, he was given a mental health diagnosis of Intermittent Explosive Disorder based on the verbal information given regarding his history at other residences. The Mental Health worker stated that she had written Mr. Lovelace's previous residence, requesting additional information, but had not received anything to date.

After reading your letter and the attached article, it is obvious that Mr. Lovelace is mentally retarded. Therefore, in an attempt to obtain information that would make him eligible for services in our system, I have secured releases from Mr. Lovelace to request information from the Central Virginia Training Center, Burrell Home for Adults, Kennedy House, and Little Ponderosa Home for Adults. In addition, I have requested that Mr. Lovelace's Mental Health worker arrange for him to have a complete psychological [evaluation] done as soon as possible, which she has agreed to do.

Mr. Lovelace was referred to the Department of Rehabilitative Services to be screened for placement at the New River Valley Workshop several months ago by his Mental Health worker. [He] has made contact with Mr. Lovelace and will be able to assist us more fully once information, such as a current psychological, has been obtained. I have asked one of my case managers to follow up on this to see if we can, perhaps, speed up this process.

I wanted to let you know where things stood at this point with Mr. Lovelace; as soon as further developments occur, I will contact you immediately. Mr. Lovelace is a lucky man to have a friend such as you; I know that he appreciates your concern and involvement, as do we as an agency. . . .

One of the first things that Cathi Drinkard did on John's behalf was to assign him to a case manager who made all the difference for him.

Diane Williamson is more than a competent professional. She does her work with a sense of mission and personal commitment. During my first conversation with her , I sensed that she would prove to be a real advocate for John, and my impression proved accurate. More than any other one person, she did the important work that improved John's life.

By June 1990, Diane had located a vacancy in what is the nicest adult home that I have ever visited. It was established decades ago by local philanthropists as a nursing home for the care of the severely disabled and the dependent elderly citizens of the small community of Dublin, Virginia. It is not far from Draper Valley. John was cared for as well as resources would allow at Draper Valley, and I believe that he was cared about. But I was very happy when Diane was able to find a place for him at the Fairview Adult Home. Not only do the staff there seem to genuinely care about the residents, but it is clean and as cheerful as a place can be that is a home to people whose health and life circumstances are so different from the norm. And, as John told me in a letter shortly after he moved there, ". . . Fairview is nice to me. I usually go to the smoking room and then to my room. Its' good food here, it's *hot*. They give me some more if I ask for it. I like it alright here."

Chapter 13

Ethics, Powerlessness, and Informed Consent

In 1981 a pair of conjoined twins, most often referred to as Siamese twins, were born in Danville, Illinois. On the order of the parents, one of whom was a physician, the infants, who were joined together below the waist, were not given the immediate medical treatment they needed to optimize their chances of survival. Nourishment was also withheld from them. The parents felt that it was best that the twins be allowed to die because of their condition. The State of Illinois interceded in the case and was awarded custody of the children. The parents and their pediatrician were indicted for attempted murder but not convicted.

In 1982 an infant with Down's syndrome was born in Bloomington, Indiana. The child had an additional complication: His esophagus was incompletely developed, so nourishment could not pass through it into the baby's stomach. Though the condition was completely correctable through surgery, the parents refused to permit the operation, preferring the death of the child because of his mental retardation. The parents' decision was upheld by several courts. The child, who had become known as Baby Doe, died before a final judicial appeal could be completed.

In 1983 a baby girl who came to be called Baby Jane Doe was also denied surgery. She had been born with both spina bifida and hydrocephalus, as well as other physical complications, and she was diagnosed as mentally retarded. A Long Island judge ruled that life-prolonging surgery should be performed on the child even though this was not the wish of the parents. An appeals court supported the will of the parents and overturned the lower court decision.

During the decade of the eighties, more and more cases like these came to the attention of the public, making the withholding of treatment and nourishment from newborns with severe disabilities a political issue, and during the Reagan administration, orders were issued to hospitals and medical personnel restricting the practice of pediatric euthanasia and providing mechanisms for reporting suspected or known cases.

Though the issue of pediatric euthanasia came to public attention during the eighties, this medical practice had orginated earlier. In 1973 researchers R. S. Duff and A. G. Campbell reported in the *New England Journal of Medicine* that 14% of the infants who died in the Yale–New Haven Medical Center from January 1970 to January 1972 died as a result of intentional withholding of treatment. A 1982 article in the *Archives of Childhood Disease* reported comparable results from a study in a British hospital, where more than 20% of the infant deaths resulted from withdrawal or withholding of treatment. According to the article, "Simply stated, about one-fifth of all neonatal deaths or 1–2 infants for every 1,000 infants born alive are being allowed to die." Even these figures may not portray the actual magnitude of pediatric euthanasia. It has been estimated that approximately 100,000 babies with serious disabilities are born in the United States each year. Though a significant number of these children would certainly die even with the best of treatment and the most heroic measures, many observers believe that the withholding of treatment and life-sustaining nourishment is causing the deaths of more of these infants each year.

In discussions of the ethics of medical care for newborns who are severely mentally retarded or otherwise seriously disabled, a common theme concerns the projected quality of life of these infants. Advocates of what has been called the quality-of-life position argue that decisions concerning euthanasia should be based on the prospective enjoyment and meaningfulness that the person in question is likely to experience by continuing to live. This, they argue, must be weighed against the suffering the person is expected to experience and the degree to which he or she will be a burden to the family and to society. Thus, from this perspective, human life is defined essentially by factors of "fitness" to live. The philosopher and ethicist Joseph Fletcher was a strong proponent of this position. In his book *Humanhood: Essays in Biomedical Ethics,* for example, he listed as criteria by which a life could be considered to be of human quality the following characteristics:

- minimal intelligence (an I.Q. higher than 20)
- self-awareness
- self-control
- a sense of time
- a sense of the past
- the capacity to relate to others
- concern for others
- communication
- control of existence
- curiosity
- a balance of rationality

Again, I have worked in special education and rehabilitation settings for many years. If these criteria were strictly applied to the children and adults whom I have seen develop into happy and productive people, most of them would not be considered human. The social, intellectual, and physical challenges they face would so hamper their performance in most of these areas that they would fail to meet the criteria for humanhood. Indeed, Fletcher contended that any individual with Down's syndrome, for example, is not a person. He argued that an individual with the social and intellectual limitations associated with this condition is simply not, according to his criteria, a human personality.

If an individual must manifest all of these qualities and abilities or be reasonably expected to manifest them by the time he or she reaches maturity to meet the definition of possessing a quality life, many functioning adults would fail to qualify as human beings. In fact I have known many people with advanced degrees who, I am convinced, would fail this test!

A major concern with the quality-of-life position on pediatric euthanasia centers on the elasticity of the term *quality.* Some critics fear that the term will be arbitrarily invoked against people who have no power to defend themselves. That, daily, some individuals' lives are judged to be of less value than others' is undeniable. A culture that overly values youth will devalue people who are considered old. A culture that sets narrow standards of beauty will devalue people considered to be ugly. A culture that worships wealth will devalue those who are poor. A culture that narrowly defines productivity will look down on those considered unproductive. A culture obsessed with personal independence will devalue the dependent, in some cases even the very young and very old. Professor Wolf Wolfensberger of Syracuse University has argued that all devalued people are literally in danger of their lives: that people whose social roles have not been "valorized"—assigned some value rather than being devalued—are constantly at risk.

In the case of infants who are born with disabilities, arbitrary standards of quality of life may influence decisions made about their care and treatment. In addition, bias may influence predictions of infants' ability to eventually meet those standards in their later development. Physicians and parents alike may be more influenced by misconceptions and stereotypes about disabilities than by factual information about the realities of living with mental retardation or other disabilities. Prognostications concerning the quality of life of a newborn with disabilities may be overly pessimistic.

Those most often involved in deciding whether or not an infant with a disability will be denied treatment or nourishment are the parents, physicians, and, in most cases that become public, the courts. Arguments have been made both for and against the participation of each of these parties in making such decisions.

Support for parents' involvement in such decisions is usually based on the concept that children are the property of their parents, who therefore have the final say on any crucial matter concerning their progeny. Critics of this view assert that parents facing such a dilemma may be emotionally distraught and may lack adequate information on which to base their decision. As a result, their fears about raising the child, concerns about the impact of the disabled child on other family members, and anxiety over the child's continuing dependency may unduly influence their decision.

Physicians are often perceived as being the most informed and appropriate parties for making objective decisions concerning pediatric euthanasia. In fact, however, they may most often be motivated by wanting to prevent suffering in the family. They may, therefore, be acting more as the family's agent than as the infant's physician. With this conflict of roles in mind, some have argued that physicians should not make the decisions in these cases, as their duty is to preserve life rather than to judge which lives deserve preservation.

Courts become involved in these life-and-death decisions when jurists are asked to determine whether or not a handicapped child is entitled to the same protection under the law as any other citizen. The decisions in such cases have been less than consistent. In some cases courts have ordered extraordinary forms of treatment (for example, in the lower court's action on Baby Jane Doe in New York). In other cases they have allowed easily correctable physical problems to go untreated, resulting in the infant's death (such as in the case of Baby Doe in Indiana).

The issue of pediatric euthanasia and handicapped newborns came to public awareness back in the early 1970s. The most visible case, one that stirred considerable controversy, involved a child born with Down's syndrome at Johns Hopkins University Hospital. The infant began vomiting shortly after birth. Further examination disclosed a blockage in the child's intestinal tract, a condition referred to as duodenal atresia. This blockage could have been removed surgically with minimal risk to the baby. Not removing it made normal digestion and nourishment impossible. The parents in this case decided not to have the surgery performed, and to withhold treatment. Except for the atresia and the physical characteristics of Down's syndrome, the child was otherwise in normal health. Following the parents' decision, all feeding and fluid tubes were disconnected from the child. He died fifteen days later of starvation and dehydration.

Surely this is a case of life-and-death discrimination against a child because of mental retardation. This baby died because, in addition to the duodenal atresia, he was mentally retarded. A child with duodenal atresia who did not show evidence of mental retardation would without question have been given the appropriate surgery, even if it were against the wishes of the parents.

In 1973 the American Association on Mental Retardation responded to this and other similar cases as follows:

> It is our position that the existence of mental retardation is no justification for the terminating of the life of any human being or for permitting such a life to be terminated either directly or through the withholding of life sustaining procedures.

The issue of pediatric euthanasia is an important one for professionals in the field of special education. The Johns Hopkins case and others have been cited widely in college and graduate school classrooms for almost two decades now as illustrations of ethical dilemmas of concern to special educators. In most undergraduate and graduate training programs, students preparing to become special educators are taught that one of their professional roles will be that of an advocate, a voice, for the rights of people with disabilities. With regard to pediatric euthanasia of infants with disabilities, however, the question of the nature and extent of the special educator's role as advocate has been viewed as more complex and difficult by professionals in the field. Many are troubled at the idea of taking a position on a matter that has traditionally been the province of parents, physicians, and the courts.

Conversations with my colleagues, however, have convinced me that teachers need to be heard on this issue. Parents, physicians, lawyers, and judges have rarely had the experience of living or working with mentally retarded individuals across the course of their lives. Special educators serving people with disabilities from infancy through adulthood have the opportunity to observe that mental retardation, in the absence of severe and chronic disease or other physical problems, does not necessarily cause lives of suffering or less value. Their direct experience with persons who are mentally retarded also shows them that the condition does not, in and of itself, justify termination of a life. Interaction with mentally retarded people tends to convince their families, teachers, and others that all people can learn, all can participate to some degree in the wide range of human experiences, and most can become valuable citizens of whatever niche in society they come to inhabit. In other words, people who have the opportunity to genuinely know mentally retarded individuals come to truly value them.

With these thoughts in mind, and after more conversations with one of my closest colleagues, Dr. Ed Polloway, I asked the Board of Directors of the Mental Retardation Division of the Council for Exceptional

Children to consider approving a position statement on the rights of people with mental retardation to medical care and treatment to sustain their lives. The board approved the following position statement in June 1988, publishing it in the journal *Education and Training of the Mentally Retarded* in March 1989:

> The Board of Directors of the Division on Mental Retardation of the Council for Exceptional Children resolves that the fact that a person is born with mental retardation or acquires mental retardation during development is not a justifiable reason, in and of itself, for terminating the life of that person. Mental retardation alone is not a nullification of quality or worth in an individual's life and should not be used as a rationale for the termination of life through direct means nor the withholding of nourishment or life-sustaining procedures.

As John Lovelace's experiences show, this issue touches the lives of both children *and* adults with mental retardation.

Making life-and-death decisions about adults with mental retardation involves essentially the same issues as for children. Again, the parents (or other family members), physicians, and courts may be involved, and the same concerns discussed earlier for each may apply. However, some mentally retarded adults may not have family members to participate in the decision making. This may be particularly true for the older residents of both institutions and community placements. In some cases the decision to give or withhold treatment may rest with a group of professionals charged with making recommendations to an institutional administrator or legal counsel. Ironically, I have found that the rights of the remaining residents of some large state institutions seem to be more carefully protected in this regard than those of the people discharged into community placements. Deinstitutionalization was motivated in part by concerns over the risks of impersonalization and abuse in institutional settings. Yet those who remain in them may be safer from these dangers than those who were removed to the community! John Lovelace's case is a clear example.

A concept that has come to be pivotal in treatment decisions is that of "informed consent." In the case of children who are mentally retarded, the parents have the right to informed consent—that is, the right to understand the likely consequences of treatment (or nontreatment) options for their child and for the rest of the family. Obviously, the accuracy and completeness of the information that is made available are critical. This raises questions about who is competent to project a child's probable future and what safeguards are needed in the process of providing information. Again, the same considerations apply for adults with mental retardation. In John's case, did the physician explain in detail the meaning of the no-code order that he presented to John? Even if he went through the motions of explanation, did John have the ability to understand what he was being told? And if he understood the information, was his decision influenced by the fact that an authority figure—the physician—was suggesting that this was the proper thing to do?

Informed consent is such an important and complex issue for people with mental retardation and their families in making treatment decisions that the American Association on Mental Retardation published a *Consent Handbook* in 1977. The *Consent Handbook* defines informed consent as having three elements: capacity, information, and voluntariness. All three elements must be present for consent to be considered valid.

The first element, capacity, is determined by three factors: the person's age, his or her competence, and the particular situation. Obviously, in the case of a child, the parents or guardians must be involved in the granting of informed consent. An infant cannot participate in the process at all, whereas an older child might, to some extent. Someone who has reached legal majority (usually eighteen years old) but who is mentally retarded may still be under the guardianship of her or his parents, who will, of course, then still be a part of the process. Here, the second factor, competence, comes into play. If someone has been judged incompetent to give informed consent, age becomes an insufficient measure of capacity. The third factor, the particular situation, may become relevant to the question of capacity when the retarded individual has no next of kin or guardian, and a professional or committee must independently determine what is in the individual's best interests.

John Lovelace signed a document, a no-code order, that indicated that he did not wish to receive treatment to save his life in a medical emergency. It documented that in the case of a stroke or heart attack it was his wish that his life not be saved. Though diagnosed as mentally retarded and institutionalized for more than twenty years, he had never been declared incompetent and he did not have a legal guardian. He had no trace of a family. John Lovelace had the legal right to sign the document, but I do not believe that he had the capacity to make the decision that it reflected. I think that asking him to sign it was a travesty of justice. I fear that many other people in the same circumstances have wrongfully been asked and are being asked to do the same.

The second element of consent, as defined by the *Consent Handbook,* is information. This concerns both *what* information is given and *how* it is given. The person should be told fully and accurately the consequences of treatment options, in a manner appropriate to his or her background and capacity. I do not know, of course, what transpired during the physician's conversation with John about the no-code order, but I do know how much difficulty I have had explaining to him things far less complex than life or death.

About the third element of informed consent, voluntariness, the author of the *Consent Handbook* says that for a person to voluntarily consent he or she must be "so situated as to be able to exercise free power of choice without intervention of any element of force, fraud, deceit, duress . . . or other ulterior form of constraint or coercion." With few exceptions, John's life has been filled with events of force, duress, constraint, and coercion. He has surely encountered fraud and deceit as well. John learned that his only means of assertion and defense was lashing out in elemental, and ultimately self-destructive, ways. He has experienced very little free choice. He has lived most of his life in settings where almost everyone had more power than he. He has lived a life of routines prescribed for him by professionals and others who have decided what is best for him. I am certain that he would sign any document that I asked him to sign. I suspect that he did the same for the physician. I am certain that thousands of powerless mentally retarded people in similar situations have signed similar documents.

Chapter 14

Caring Friends, Blindness, and Pieces of Purgatory

Besides being a competent case manager with the New River Valley Community Services Board, Diane Williamson truly became a friend to John. It was through her efforts that he eventually went to work at the New River Valley Workshop. Finally, he was going to be working! His activity at the workshop began with an extended period of evaluation to determine his level of abilities and the kind of work that he would be best suited for there. He seemed to enjoy this and apparently worked hard at doing well at the various tasks he was given. After only a short while, however, his participation was interrupted. He broke his glasses again and could not see well enough to work. Getting his glasses repaired took several weeks, and by then John was anxious to get back to work. As he wrote in a letter in July 1990, "I am doing alright, but am waiting to go back to work. I will be glad when I return to work."

I went to visit John at the New River Valley Workshop after he did return. He seemed very happy there, and both the other workers and the staff showed him real friendship. His task was folding cloth shopping bags for packing and shipping. He seemed proud of his work, showing me each step and how important it was to make sure that it was done correctly. I remember clearly my drive home that afternoon, feeling that, finally, things seemed to be coming together for John. He had a nice place to live and he was working! How grateful I was for the help that Diane Williamson had given John. She was making a real difference in his life.

Camp Virginia Jaycee had remained an important part of my relationship with John. Each fall and spring, John was there as a camper. He had a special relationship with the students. Some kept returning each semester and looked forward to seeing him again. Other students who were new to the camp had learned about John from their friends. The story of John's no-code order had become part of the lore of the camp weekend and John was an instant celebrity when he arrived.

In anticipation of the camping weekend in 1991, I wrote to John to let him know the dates and that arrangements for his attendance were being worked out. In early February I received a reply that John had dictated to Diane. It contained disturbing news.

> How are you Dave? I got your letter here at Fairview. I want you to come down here and see me.
>
> I can't work now because I can't see. I don't know if I can come to camp or not.
>
> . . . Doctors say my eyes are bad. We will just have to wait and see about the workshop.
>
> Fairview is nice to me. I usually go to the smoking room and then to my room. It's good food here, it's *hot*. They give me some more if I ask for it. I like it alright here.
>
> I really would like to see you sometime. Please write me back soon.
>
> Love,
> John

A few weeks earlier John's behavior and general health had deteriorated rapidly. I learned later that he had appeared disoriented and had been wetting his pants regularly. He had also started to lash out at people again. When he was finally hospitalized, the reason for these changes became apparent. John's vision had been poor for a long time. Now, however, he was blind. Medical reports indicated that his ability to see had declined rapidly and dramatically. According to a neurologist's report,

> His mental status today reveals that he is quite worried about his upcoming eye examination tomorrow and is specifically worried that he will undergo surgery and become completely blind there.

> He is probably legally blind in the right eye due to cloudy ocular media.

The next day he was examined by an ophthalmologist, whose report was, of course, more detailed. Among his observations were the following:

> *Impression*
> 1. Blind right eye
> 2. Corneal dystrophy, both eyes
> 3. Cataract, left eye
> 4. Borderline, left eye

A more telling indication of the changes in John's life came from the registered nurse who supervised his care while he was in the hospital. Her summary comments read:

> Patient is blind—needs direction and assistance to walk and with all activities of daily living. Needs someone to light cigarettes. Generally is pleasant and cooperative. Needs food prepared for him before he begins to eat.

This disturbing new development in John's life seemed to come just when things were beginning to go well for him. He finally had a job in a good environment, and he was living in the best adult home that I had seen. I reflected a great deal during this time about the no-code order, my questioning of it, the relationship that John and I had developed, and the seemingly endless difficulties he faced. I was confused and depressed.

John came to the weekend at Camp Virginia Jaycee in March. I had tried to prepare the students for the changes that they would see in him. I explained his blindness, and we talked about how it might be affecting him emotionally. I was impressed with their enthusiasm over trying to make the weekend the best possible for him given his increased need for assistance.

John's behavior over the weekend was very different from what it had been in previous years. Not only did he need more help moving about, dressing, eating, lighting his cigarettes, and doing other basic tasks, but he was sadder and seemed much older than I had ever seen

John at Camp Jaycee after Losing His Sight

him. Camp Jaycee had always been a place where he smiled and laughed, even when things were not going well elsewhere in his life. He now appeared worn out, exhausted with the new disabilities he faced. He spent much of the time bent over in his chair with his head between his legs. He burned his fingers several times trying to smoke, and his counselors told me that he cried one night when he wet his pants while trying to use the urinal. Overall, he seemed broken. I tried to remain positive in my talks with him, but I don't think I was convincing. My students once again made me proud. They were constantly helpful and encouraging with John. Their manner with him was a beautiful blend of grandchild to grandparent, loving friend, and gentle parent. I came home after the weekend feeling a powerful mix of emotions.

In May of 1991, John was declared legally blind by the Virginia Department for the Visually Handicapped. This classification made him eligible for services that would help him adapt to his visual disability. He soon began to get training to help him move around Fairview. He was taught how to find the dining room, smoking lounge, and bathroom independently, and given assistance in managing his room and belongings. This assistance proved of great help to him both in his daily living skills and in his emotional life. As he became somewhat more independent, his morale improved.

To learn to adjust to his new circumstances, John also attended the Developmental Day Services program in the New River Valley. This program for people who are more severely disabled was the best choice for John after it was deemed no longer feasible for him to work at the workshop. He attended Developmental Day Services for many months and enjoyed the activities there immensely.

John and I corresponded fairly regularly during this time. He always had someone write for him and I always learned who that person was as another point of connection with him. I sometimes wrote a note to his corresponder on the letters that I sent to John; sometimes this was Diane Williamson, at other times someone who worked at Fairview Home.

In May he wrote:

> It was good to hear from you. It would be great to see you in July, maybe for my birthday.
>
> I am doing better now, I have a new roommate at Fairview, we get along real good. I was also promoted to group three at the Day Program, the people in this group are nice to me.
>
> Hope to see you soon, I am excited about camp this summer. [He was spending a full week at Virginia Jaycee that summer.]
>
> Sincerely,
> John

I couldn't visit John on his birthday, as I had to travel, but I wrote to him in early July and sent him an early birthday present: some cash, at his request.

In early August, I sent John his birth certificate as a present. I had asked him many months earlier to sign a form so that I could send for a copy of his birth certificate. I felt that it was an important thing for him to have, as a symbol of his life. As far as I know, he still has it hanging on his wall. The only other symbols he has of his life are a few pictures, mostly from Camp Virginia Jaycee; a few craft projects, again from camp; and a copy of Mike Hudson's newspaper article about him.

Shortly after I sent the birth certificate, Diane called to let me know that John would soon have another case manager. Diane, who had also married by then, had decided to return to school to pursue a graduate degree in special education. She continued to stay in touch with John, however, and was a genuine friend. John also found other friends around this time, as is evident in a letter I wrote to him in November 1991.

Dear John:

Thank you for your nice letter. I really enjoyed hearing from you. It was good to hear that things are going so well at Fairview. I was sorry to hear, though, that you have had a bad cold. I hope that you are better by now.

I really enjoyed seeing you at Camp Jaycee. All the Lynchburg College students liked seeing you also. Have you heard from any of them?

Enclosed is $50 to be used for cigarettes as you need them. I am asking Phyllis Bessler [an employee at Fairview] to help you with this. This money was given by the guys in a fraternity here at Lynchburg College called Sigma Mu Sigma. You know many of them from Camp Jaycee. Jim Farrell collected the money and brought it by today. It is a wonderful present and it shows how much they like you. . . .

I will write you again next week to let you know when I can make my Christmas visit. I will be bringing you a small present, and we will go to lunch at McDonald's.

Take care my friend. I look forward to seeing you in a couple of weeks.

Sincerely,
Dave

After my move to South Carolina in June 1992, I wrote to John regularly and talked with him occasionally on the telephone. Things seemed to continue to go well for him, and I remained convinced that Fairview was the best home that John had found since his childhood home with the Hunters. In fact, I still believe Fairview is the finest adult home that I have ever visited.

Mitzi Thorne, who took over for Diane as John's case manager after Diane left, proved competent and concerned. She wrote to me for John and kept me informed about her visits with him and how he was doing. Her reports tended to be cautiously optimistic. She told me on several occasions that John continued to be frustrated with the additional disabilities he was encountering because of his blindness. She felt, however, that he was responding well to the individual assistance he was getting to learn to be as independent as possible.

In February 1993, however, Mitzi called with a message that was obviously difficult for her to deliver. It was also painful for me to receive. John was being dismissed from Fairview. He had again resorted to expressing his frustrations in angry outbursts, cursing, kicking, and swinging his fists at other residents and employees. Mitzi had been given notice that she would have to find another place for him to live.

Mitzi called twenty-five adult homes in several areas of Virginia before she found one that would take John. At each one that she called, the administrator asked why he was being moved and, when told of his history with other adult homes, refused to take him. Mitzi was candid with me about the placement she had found for John: It was not like Fairview, but it was the best she could do.

This outcome distressed Mitzi, who felt that she had personally failed John. I assured her that John's difficulties have resulted from systemic and long-standing social problems. Mitzi's efforts on John's behalf went far beyond a salary or job description. They are to be applauded.

My first visit to John in his new home was another lesson in the "pieces of purgatory" that are replacing large centralized institutions as repositories for many of the poor, old, and damaged in our society.

I followed the directions to John's new home and pulled my car into a visitors' space in the parking lot. The building was attractive from the outside, and the front doors opened into a pleasant reception area. There was no receptionist at the desk. I walked down the main hall past attractively decorated rooms looking for someone who could help me find John. I saw nobody until I came to a bright dining area. A staff member came over immediately and asked if she could help me.

I explained that I was there to visit John Lovelace. She looked puzzled for a moment, then said, "We don't have him here; he must be up on the hill." She took me to a door and pointed me toward another, larger building. When I asked her to check the records to make sure he wasn't in this building, she explained that there were only 45 people there and she knew them all by name. "This is a nursing home for those who can pay," she explained. "Up on the hill is the home for adults. Same name but up there are people who can't pay." She told me that there were 160 people living there.

I walked to the building on the hill. The attendant had told me in detail how to find the door that would be unlocked. "They don't get so many visitors up there," she said. As I opened the door, I was overwhelmed by cigarette smoke and the smell of urine and disinfectant. I was also struck by the almost startled look of staff members at the appearance of a stranger.

I asked for directions, and after some confusion I was led to John's room by a woman wearing the kind of institutional uniform (white polyester pants and top, and white shoes) that today is rarely seen in "normalized" state residential facilities. My first glimpse of John was of him sitting on the edge of his bed with his head in his hands. One of his roommates was sitting on his bed rocking in an autistic fashion. Another was sitting on a towel in a wheelchair, naked from the waist down, in excrement. I was assured that an "accident" had just happened.

I spent several hours with John that day. As best I could determine, he spends each day dividing his time among his own room, the dining hall, and the smoking/TV room. The smoking room consists of rows of wooden benches, free-standing ashtrays, and a wall-mounted television—an arrangement I have seen in other adult homes. The room can probably accommodate fifty people. The intensity of the smoke coming from the room into the hallway was staggering.

During meals one of the uniformed staff members helps John. He seems to eat well, and while I was there he was given patient assistance and encouragement in the dining hall. While John was having lunch, I tried to talk with the staff members who seemed most interested in him, hoping to find someone who would write letters for him. None of these people seemed willing to make that commitment. They may have been afraid of becoming overly involved in a resident's life, and they already seemed stretched to the limit by the high staff-to-resident ratio. Whatever the reason, I was unable to establish a contact among the staff.

When I write to John now, I don't receive a reply. When I send him gifts, no one acknowledges that he has received them. Between visits, I know nothing of what is happening in his life. I often wonder if John's life is better today in any way than it was on the day I met him. I wonder, too, at his ability to survive the pain of his days.

Chapter 15

Policies, People, and No Room in the Graveyard

In 1972, the U.S. Congress passed legislation entitled Supplemental Security Income for the Aged, the Disabled, and the Blind. By the time it went into effect in 1974, politicians, bureaucrats, and professionals in the human services already knew it simply as SSI. The program provides income to people who, because of age or disability, are unable to enter the work force. Though the program is fully funded with federal money, states may, if they choose, pay supplemental amounts to recipients to compensate for variations in the cost of living from state to state. Most state supplements are relatively modest.

Though the program was designed to help individuals with disabilities, and in many cases it surely has, it also greatly fueled the movement toward deinstitutionalization. It provided a means for states to discharge people from mental retardation and mental health institutions into communities at very little cost to themselves. Indeed, it became an attractive means of saving state money. When people were discharged from institutions into communities, the states saved the daily costs of institutionalization, while the costs of living in the community were covered largely by federal SSI dollars. In the first few years of SSI's existence, the deinstitutionalization of people with mental retardation or mental illness increased dramatically. John Lovelace was among those who left for the community during this exodus.

And so SSI made it much easier for states to discharge people from institutions, to save themselves money by doing so, and to make minimal investments in supporting these people in the community. SSI does not set standards for the care and treatment of people after they leave institutions. Theoretically, the SSI benefit is paid directly to the recipient. In reality, the checks are usually signed over to adult home operators or other housing providers, and the residents are given only a small allowance. The recipients are presumed to be free to "shop" for the best living arrangements and, thus, to make the best choices for themselves in care and treatment. This free-market approach to the needs of people who are mentally retarded, however, has led to the kinds of problems discussed in this book. Although Virginia established a system of community services boards to provide safeguards and assistance to mentally retarded people in the community, funding restraints severely limit what small professional staffs can do with large caseloads. SSI shifted the fiscal burden for housing people with mental retardation largely to the federal government and diminished the involvement of the states in the care of these people. The SSI legislation stipulated only age and disability requirements for recipients. It did nothing to encourage the development of quality living arrangements or meaningful community programs for these people. In fact, it encouraged the development of an industry of largely unmonitored and often substandard adult homes. The positive vision of deinstitutionalization was in many cases tarnished and even made a travesty.

In the process of trying to be of help to John Lovelace, and to understand the meaning of his situation, I called on my friend Elliot Schewel several times. Elliot has been a businessman and public servant throughout his adult life. As a member of the Virginia Senate for many years, he has been concerned with issues of fiscal responsibility in government and the well-being of the public in other regards. He has always been willing to help me find answers to questions, and he has always been responsive to requests for assistance from others who have come to him through me. He has my deepest respect and gratitude.

To help me find answers to questions about the no-code order in John's case, Elliot asked the commissioner of Mental Health and Mental Retardation for Virginia, Howard Cullum, to look into the case. The answers were encouraging. There is an increasing awareness of the need to protect the rights of people with mental retardation in the community. More advocates are being employed to monitor their rights and investigate possible violations. Nonetheless, the resources for such protection are limited, and the safeguards are, therefore, fragile. I believe that this is particularly true for people like John who were previously institutionalized, and who thereby lost contact with family and friends who would normally have looked out for their welfare. Many of these same people were never declared incompetent during their institutionalization. They were then discharged without legal guardians and could, as John was, be called on to make life-affecting decisions without caring assistance or legal protection.

Around the time that Mike Hudson's series was being published, I asked Elliot Schewel to contact the commissioner a second time, this time concerning the overall quality of care in adult homes in Virginia. Elliot had read Mike's series and was more than willing to inquire about what Virginia was doing to correct the situation. He pointed out to the commissioner that despite ten years of government studies and reports on adult homes in Virginia, no action had been taken.

Elliot's inquiry resulted in efforts, which I have been assured continue, to monitor the living conditions in adult homes. The licensing standards for these homes are being raised, and the services funded through Virginia's community services boards have increased. But the bottom line remains that most of the limited funding for community living for mentally retarded persons comes from SSI, which provides no standards or expectations for quality care, treatment, and protection for recipients.

When Commissioner Cullum responded to Elliot, he sent a copy of a plan to improve adult homes that he had already been diligently working on. His best efforts, however, were limited, because he was trying to deal with the problem at the state level whereas it is national policies and practices that actually determine the possibilities for improvement and reform in services to people who are mentally retarded. My letter to Senator Schewel in November 1989 after he sent me a copy of this document expresses my sense of these limitations.

Dear Elliot:

Thanks for sending the copy of Howard Cullum's letter and his *Plan for Addressing the Needs of the Mentally Disabled Residents of Homes for Adults.* I have reviewed the plan and I believe there is a great deal of merit in what it proposes. I think that the two most important issues it speaks to are licensing and financing. The proposed plan is a move in the right direction but it seems to me that it should address more strongly and clearly the urgent need for reform in the licensing of adult homes and an increase in the financial resources provided for the care of the mentally disabled people living in these homes.

As Mike Hudson illustrated so compellingly in his *Roanoke Times and World-News* series, there are essentially no teeth in the existing licensing practices for homes for adults in Virginia. It appears that obtaining a license is a simple matter. Losing a license is a rarity. There are no real penalties short of revocation. Revocation has apparently occurred only in cases of extreme and chronic violations of standards. The standards are far from being rigorous. I believe that this is a critical matter that deserves close attention.

Howard Cullum states in his letter to you that the bottom line is financial. He is absolutely correct in this observation. Most of the adult homes that Virginians with mental disabilities live in are essentially small businesses operating for profit. It is staggering to consider that these homes are expected to provide room, board, supervision, recreation, and other daily needs for people who often have serious and multiple problems, all . . . for less than $20 per day. Somewhere in that less than $20, of course, a profit must be found. It is not difficult to understand, given this context, the appalling conditions and poor nutritional practices which have been found in some of these homes. The funding available for people living in adult homes in Virginia is part of a national problem that must be addressed at the federal level. As you know, support for people who were deinstitutionalized as part of the national movement did not follow people from institutions into the community. I trust that soon we will be seeing significant movement at the national level to improve the situation. I think that action must come now in Virginia, however, to do what can be done to provide a more decent level of support for people who have been largely ignored in recent years.

Elliot, I would appreciate any support you could lend to measures that would improve life for those people in Virginia who because of disabilities and other circumstances must live in adult homes. In particular, I believe that your attention to how adult homes are licensed, how they are inspected, how standards are enforced, and how financial support might be increased could be of great value to these people. Thanks for taking the time to consider these comments.

Writing letters is easier than battling the political and financial realities that face the legislators and state administrators who are dealing with the problems that my letter articulated. Elliot Schewel and Howard Cullum continue their labors and are making a difference. As Elliot concluded in his reply to my letter: "As you can see, the pace of progress is very, very slow but I am hopeful that when money becomes a little more available we will be able to make more meaningful strides to come up with solutions to these issues. That doesn't help much but it's all I can report at this time."

Two other requests that I made to state governmental agencies may illuminate some of the curious effects of deinstitutionalization. Both requests were related to what I perceived to be John's best interests.

The first request came during one of the times when I was wondering if finding a really good adult home for John to live in was even possible. The safeguards and services that John needed seemed unavailable in a community setting. Discouraged, I decided that John would actually be better off back in a state institution, where at least the system of resident advocacy that had been developed would ensure that nothing like the no-code order would occur. The reforms achieved in the seventies and eighties, I thought, made life for a person like John safer inside an institution than outside. It was a humbling conclusion for a professor who had, over those same decades, been telling his students about the ills of institutions.

It was with a great sense of irony that I broached the subject quietly with administrators at the Central Virginia Training Center. Here I was actually asking that John be readmitted to the same institution from which he had been released fifteen years earlier to a life of greater "normality" in the community. The irony was short lived. I was quickly informed that there was no chance that John would be readmitted. It simply could not be done.

I made the second request after having a conversation with a community services board case manager about the death of a man she had worked with for several years. She explained that final arrangements for people living in adult homes are often difficult to make. In many cases, there are no next of kin and no resources to provide even the most modest of burials. Whether or not a person ends up in a pauper's grave depends on the resources and customs of the locality in which the person dies. Cremation is sometimes the least expensive, and, therefore, the most desirable, alternative. The case manager told me of the death of a man whose case she had managed for many years after his discharge from a state institution. When he died, his remains were cremated, and his ashes delivered to her office. Uncertain what to do with them, she put the container on a shelf, where it had been collecting dust for five years.

This story disturbed me greatly and got me thinking about what would happen when John died. The idea of an impersonal burial for him was difficult to think about.

Most of the older residential institutions in our country have their own cemeteries, a fact that I think indicates the degree to which these places were separated from the mainstream of society. Not only did they have walls and gates to keep people in or out, but they needed their own graveyards because many residents' ties to outside relatives had often been completely severed by the time they died. The graves in the cemeteries were usually identified only by a metal marker bearing a number that administrators recorded in a ledger.

Beginning in the 1970s, the metal markers at the Central Virginia Training Center were replaced with granite headstones. This gesture of respect probably went unrecognized by most people outside of the institution, but many of the longtime employees of the institution told me how much it meant to them, and to the residents. It was seen as a sign of respect.

The first time I visited the cemetery, I was struck by the beauty of the site. Located on several gently rolling hills, it is surrounded by ancient oaks and has a feeling of age and a strange sense of continuity to it. As I walked through it, I thought of the changes that institutions have undergone in our country, and the various reasons people have lived, and died, in them. Carrie Buck's mother is buried there. She died the same year that I was born. I wondered what she understood of the fate of her daughter and the significance that her sterilization had for the world.

I decided that I would ask the director of the Central Virginia Training Center if arrangements could be made so that when John died he could be buried in the CVTC cemetery. (The CVTC cemetery seemed appropriate for John not only because the site is beautiful but because it is on the grounds of the place that was his home longer than anywhere else.) I felt that if a plot here could be arranged, I could work on the other things that would be needed, such as payment for a headstone and other funeral expenses. Just having a commitment for a space in the cemetery would comfort me. With such a commitment, the community services board might, I thought, be able to work with me to see that simple but decent provisions were made when needed.

The director of the Central Virginia Training Center at the time was Dr. Bill Walker. Bill had been helpful to me in several ways. He had, in fact, facilitated my access to John's files after John had signed a release for me to review them. He had also been interested in some of my previous work, and I had shared a copy of the book about Carrie Buck with him. When I approached him with the idea of a plot for John in the cemetery, he was open to the suggestion and willing to explore it through the appropriate channels.

A few weeks later, Bill had a response to my request: The Virginia Attorney General's office had considered it and denied it. The only reason Bill was given was that it might set a precedent that would lead to other similar requests, and this might become a burden for the state. I have trouble imagining the Commonwealth of Virginia being flooded with requests for burials on the grounds of its institutions, but I let the matter drop. I have not pursued it further. I still worry from time to time about what the end will be like for John. Then again, he may outlive me. Who knows? He may worry about what the end will be like for me.

Epilogue

While I was working on this manuscript, I read an excellent book by William F. May called *The Patient's Ordeal.* In his introduction to the book, May describes an exchange that T. S. Eliot once had with a college student—one very like the exchange I described at the beginning of this tale. Eliot had given a lecture on some serious problem in American life. During the question period following the lecture, the student asked urgently, "Mr. Eliot, what are we going to do about the problem you have discussed?" Eliot replied to the student, "You have asked the wrong question. You must understand that we face two types of problems in life. One kind of problem provokes the question 'What are we going to do about it?' The other kind poses the subtler question 'How do we behave toward it?' "

It seems clear to me that the first kind of problem can be solved with direct, sometimes simple, and immediate action. The immediate relief that a doctor or dentist may give a patient is an example of this kind of problem resolution. The second kind of problem is a greater challenge. This is a problem that has no direct, simple, or immediate solution. What do you do for a dying friend or family member? Do you avoid that person because you cannot cure his or her suffering or prevent the inevitable? Abiding by your friend or relative in such a situation requires a different approach to the problem: You must see it as a factor to be lived with as part of an enduring relationship.

When I initially tried to respond to my student's question of "What are you going to do about it?" I approached John Lovelace from the first perspective. I sought a fast and clean solution to the problem of his protection and well-being. As I came to know him, I learned that he needed more than a "quick fix" to his problems: He needed a friend. He needed a sense of connectedness that would endure his constant changes in circumstances. I suspect that this is the greatest need of many of our fellow human beings. The simple problems that can be fixed quickly are not the ones that drain us. Having people who will endure with us is one of the greatest of our human needs.

Through coming to know John Lovelace, I have gained new insights into the experience of people who are mentally retarded. I have also come to know in much more real terms the problems of the systems supposedly designed to help these people. In my lifetime, I will be able to make, at best, only a minimal difference in these systems and what they do for people. Through coming to know John Lovelace, however, I have learned more about the mysteries of human relationships. I have been strengthened in my understanding that small gestures of caring, not huge and seemingly heroic feats, are the essence of friendship. I have learned more deeply the importance of facing suffering and unsolvable problems with other people rather than avoiding people whose problems you do not have the power to make "right."

John Lovelace is my friend. We correspond only a few times a year now. I send him cards and gifts for his birthday and Christmas. I help with the expense of his cigarettes when I can. I cannot visit him as often now that I am living in South Carolina. He always asks about my health when I see him. He scolds me if I don't visit or write often enough. He calls me his friend.